To Bob

from Pat.

3/25/61

The
Amazing World
of Medicine

The Amazing World of Medicine

EDITED BY

Helen Wright *and* Samuel Rapport

HARPER & BROTHERS | *Publishers NEW YORK*

Acknowledgments

The editors acknowledge with thanks permission to use material in this book, as follows:

THE GREAT BEGINNINGS by Logan Clendening, reprinted from BEHIND THE DOCTOR by Logan Clendening, by permission of Alfred A. Knopf, Inc., copyright 1933 by Alfred A. Knopf, Inc.

LEEUWENHOEK: FIRST OF THE MICROBE HUNTERS by Paul de Kruif, reprinted from MICROBE HUNTERS, copyright 1926 by Harcourt Brace and Company, Inc.; copyright 1954 by Paul de Kruif. Used by permission of the publishers.

A PESTHOUSE IN VIENNA by Morton Thompson, from THE CRY AND THE COVENANT by Morton Thompson, copyright 1949 by Morton Thompson, reprinted by permission of Doubleday & Company, Inc.

MIRACULOUS ACCIDENT by Milton Silverman, a selection from MAGIC IN A BOTTLE by Milton Silverman, 2nd edition copyright 1958, The Macmillan Company and used with their permission.

VICTORY OVER PAIN by Victor Robinson, reprinted by permission of the publishers Abelard-Schuman Limited, from VICTORY OVER PAIN by Victor Robinson. Copyright 1946 by Henry Schuman Inc.

JOSEPH LISTER DISCOVERS ANTISEPSIS by Logan Clendening, reprinted from BEHIND THE DOCTOR by Logan Clendening, by permission of Alfred A. Knopf, Inc., copyright 1933 by Alfred A. Knopf, Inc.

FIELD HOSPITAL—WORLD WAR I by Frederick A. Pottle, from STRETCHERS; THE STORY OF A HOSPITAL UNIT ON THE WESTERN FRONT by Frederick A. Pottle, 1929 Yale University Press, reprinted by permission from Yale University Press. Copyright 1929 Yale University Press.

A SURGEON'S DOMAIN by Bertram M. Bernheim M.D., reprinted from A SURGEON'S DOMAIN by Bertram M. Bernheim M.D., by permission of W. W. Norton & Company, Inc. Copyright 1947 by W. W. Norton & Company, Inc.

SPARE PARTS FOR DEFECTIVE HEARTS by Ben Pearse, copyright 1958 by The Curtis Publishing Company, reprinted by permission from the author.

NAVY DOCTOR IN LAOS by Thomas A. Dooley, from THE EDGE OF TOMORROW by Thomas A. Dooley, copyright 1958 by Thomas A. Dooley, used by permission of the publishers, Farrar, Straus and Cudahy, Inc.

A MAN FROM MEXICO by Berton Roueché, from ELEVEN BLUE MEN, copyright 1949 by Berton Roueché, reprinted by permission of Little, Brown & Company.

TWENTY-FOUR HOURS IN A CANCER HOSPITAL by Evan McLeod Wylie, copyright 1956 by Evan McLeod Wylie, reprinted by permission of William Morris Agency, Inc. and of McCall's Magazine.

THE DEATH OF LOUIS SLOTIN by Ralph E. Lapp, from ATOMS AND PEOPLE by Ralph E. Lapp, copyright © 1956 by Ralph E. Lapp, reprinted by permission from Harper & Brothers.

THE CRUEL GAME by Heinz Gartmann, from MAN UNLIMITED by Heinz Gartmann, copyright 1957 by Pantheon Books Inc., reprinted by permission from Pantheon Books Inc.

Contents

Preface

The medicine man casts a handful of bones on the ground and notes how they fall. Or he examines the entrails of a newly killed chicken. Or he seeks portents in the stars or the weather. Then he decides on diagnosis and treatment.

The modern physician taps your chest, feels your pulse, and sticks a glass rod in your mouth. Perhaps he jabs you with a hollow needle to take a sample of your blood. Then he scribbles some hieroglyphics on a pad with the comment that you are to take one tablet three times a day.

To the hypothetical "man from Mars," the two systems might seem to have much in common. Actually, they are as far apart as the poles. One depends on mysticism, on superstition, on fear of angry gods. The other depends on a scaffold of knowledge which has been laboriously constructed through the centuries. Its timbers have often been discovered in the unlikeliest places; its girders and braces have been tested and retested and been replaced by others that have proved more effective in actual practice. One is mumbo jumbo; the other is based on an understanding of the laws of nature.

Whole libraries have been filled with the story of how this scaffold has been erected and how various parts of it have contributed to the monumental whole. Yet it is possible to single out certain great events in this story, some for their transcendent importance, others for their human drama, and these are the events which are related in the pages that follow.

As you read, we hope you will sense some of the excitement which the great discoverers must have felt when they learned some new secret of the human body or some new method of conquering disease. As you grow to understand something about how this huge reservoir of medical knowledge was collected, you are sure to have deepening respect for the dedicated servants of humanity who write the letters M.D. after their names.

THE
GREAT BEGINNINGS

The Hippocratic Oath

Of all the businesses and professions of mankind, that of the physician—to alleviate the sufferings of his fellow human beings—is surely one of the noblest. Even in the Dark Ages when physicians were ignorant of the causes of disease, when their remedies were hit-or-miss and often cruel and useless, their dedication to this service continued. From the days of Hippocrates to the present it has made them a race apart.

Hippocrates himself did not compose the Oath—parts of it were written over a period of centuries—but it is fittingly named in his honor. From the days when he ministered to the sick of Athens to the present, when young men still recite the Oath as they graduate from medical school, it has served physicians as an ethical guide. It ranks with the greatest moral statements that mankind possesses.

I swear by Apollo the Physician, by Asclepius, by Health, by Panacea and by all the gods and goddesses, making them my witnesses, that I will carry out, according to my ability and judgment, this oath and this indenture. To hold my teacher in this art equal to my own parents; to make him partner in my livelihood; when he is in need of money to share mine with him; to consider his family as my own brothers, and to teach them this art, if they want to learn it, without fee or indenture; to impart precept, oral instruction, and all other instruction to my own sons, the sons of my teacher, and to indentured pupils who have

3

taken the physician's oath, but to nobody else. I will use treatment to help the sick according to my ability and judgment, but never with a view to injury and wrong-doing. Neither will I administer a poison to anybody when asked to do so, nor will I suggest such a course. Similarly I will not give a woman a pessary to cause abortion. But I will keep pure and holy both my life and my art. I will not use the knife, not even, verily, on sufferers from stone, but I will give place to such as are craftsmen therein. Into whatsoever houses I enter, I will enter to help the sick, and I will abstain from all intentional wrong-doing and harm, especially from abusing the bodies of man or woman, bond or free. And whatsoever I shall see or hear in the course of my profession, as well as outside my profession in my intercourse with men, if it be what should not be published abroad, I will never divulge, holding such things to be holy secrets. Now if I carry out this oath, and break it not, may I gain forever reputation among all men for my life and for my art; but if I transgress it and forswear myself, may the opposite befall me.

The First Steps

by Logan Clendening

1. The Medicine Man

At the dawn of history, when our story opens, there was the medicine man—the witch doctor. He was intelligent enough to try to find some logical explanation for health and disease. What he did not understand, he attributed to supernatural powers. He believed that evil spirits could strike from afar; or by actually taking up residence in human bodies, bring on illness and death. What could be more logical than to attempt to drive such spirits away, or by a variety of means induce them to depart? Logan Clendening's fanciful story of a prehistoric operation for epilepsy is a typical example of such a "cure." Even today, as Clendening points out, similar methods are practiced by savages and ignorant peoples in remote corners of the earth.

In the dawn of time on a riverbank in the green land! Caves, piles of rudely fashioned stones, skins hung to dry—the litter of humans.

Htebh stood at the cave mouth, sadly gazing at his son. The youth was in the throes of his terrible malady again.

He had felt it coming on. That was the strange thing about this demon that possessed him. It gave warnings. The boy had known the fit was coming and had staggered up to the plot of grass under the great tree. He had learned from experience that it was safer for him to be on the grass away from stones or logs.

There he lay panting now, for the fit had passed. First he had emitted a great shout—a tortured cry of agony as his head was thrown back, his arms and legs were drawn into convulsion after convulsion which racked him, his eyes turned up, and the froth formed in his mouth.

The women came crowding to the mouth of the cave. Most of them gave one glance and went back to their work, for the wretched boy's attacks were a familiar sight by this time. Only his mother sat down and, covering her face with her hands, rocked herself to and fro, moaning.

One of the boy's brothers, coming up the steep slope from the river below, glanced at the quivering figure under the tree and laughed derisively. But Htebh rebuked him.

"Fool! And of a fool's litter!" he cried. "Do you wish to court devils? The fiend that inhabits thy brother may spawn and send some of his brood into thy head."

The awesome warning served to quiet the scoffer.

The grandmother came out of the cave and waddled over to the prostrate figure. Taking out of her bag a sharpened fishbone, she grasped the lad's arm and thrust the point of the bone into one of the veins that could be plainly seen beneath the skin. The blood flowed freely.

Htebh made no sign at this, nor any attempt to stop her. But they had tried that before. The devils which caused this malady did not flow out of the body with the blood.

"Go fetch the medicine man, Astur," he commanded the youth who had laughed.

By the time the priest and medicine man with his train of assistants could be seen coming up the river path, the sick boy was to all outward appearances perfectly well. His mother sat over him crooning and rubbing his forehead.

"The demon still tortures my son," Htebh announced to Astur.

The medicine man frowned portentously at this, as if to rebuke boy and demon both.

"I have tried everything," Htebh continued. "The demon resists all my magic. Do not forget that I have tried the incantation of the seven fishes, and still the demon returns. His blood has flown over and over again, and still the demon does not leave him."

"Ay," said the medicine man solemnly, "these devils which cause convulsions inhabit the head." Here the priest tapped his forehead. "We must give them a way to get out. We must make an opening there."

Htebh nodded in agreement and acquiescence.

"Send for Achot, the trephiner," commanded the priest.

"I know these demons," explained the medicine man while they awaited the arrival of the trephiner. "When I was young, my father pointed out to me one of our tribesmen who had been in the great battle with the warriors of the Folk Beyond the East. In the battle he had been struck on the right side of the head by a spear. The spear was flung with great force and broke the bone. But on the point of that spear the medicine worker of the Folk Beyond the East had witched a demon, and it entered the head of our tribesman and he suffered as does your boy. Hy!" Here the medicine man's voice sunk to a whisper. "Do you know something else that was strange about that demon? My father pointed it out to me and I have seen it since with my own eyes. Though the hole was in the right side of the head, it was the left arm and leg that were convulsed. These are subtle demons. They roam through all parts."

The trephiner was a man of venerable appearance. He had been brought up to do this work. His father and his father's father had been trephiners before him.

With him had come also the high priest and the headman of the tribe.

The patient was laid out on the ground. His hands and feet were bound with thongs. His head was laid on a stone.

The priest stood at his head. A circle of priests and tribesmen sat around the prostrate form. The medicine man walked round and round inside this circle chanting a religious hymn. The circle of helpers rocked back and forth emitting long-drawn wails for help.

The trephiner laid out several sharp-edged flints on a flat rock. He put some soft dried moss beside him, and, speaking gently and encouragingly to the boy, he made a swift cut through the skin of the scalp. He mopped the blood up with his dry moss and put his hand out for a glowing brand of wood which his assistant handed him from the fire. He seared the edges of the scalp wound, and the victim for the first time let out a long wail of pain. The incantations rose in volume.

Exposing the smooth plate of bone, the trephiner now took one of his sharp-edged flints and began to scrape the bone. The victim writhed a little from time to time, but did not complain much. It probably hurt him less than the dentist of our own day hurts one of his patients with his drill.

A priest came forward and put a cup of mistletoe wine to the boy's lips. He drank several cups during the operation, so that by the time the opening was completed, he was snoring happily.

The surgeon packed wet moss over the wound and left him sleeping in the cave. For several days he tossed with fever. Matter came running from the wound. The priest said it was the sign the devil inside was dying. Wine was poured on the wound. The old grandmother brought herbs from the woods to quiet the boy.

Finally the boy was able to be up and about. And, sure enough, the demons did not trouble him for all of that summer and the winter following and the next winter.

But then the demon returned. The boy had another convulsion, and the trephiner, with the help of the priest, made a hole on the opposite side of his head. For a while again there was no falling sickness, and then the boy disappeared. Search of the countryside failed to find him. Weeks later his body was found at the foot of a cliff. Probably, they said, the demon returned and attacked him as he was standing on the edge, and in his convulsion he threw himself over and was killed.

This story of mine, while it is entirely fanciful, has firm basis in reality.

Skulls with round trephine openings in them have been found in prehistoric human excavations all over the world. These holes were not made in the skull after death, because many of them show, around the edges of the opening, evidence that the bone has grown in an attempt at healing. From the same signs we decide that the trephining did not kill the patient. Some skulls show several trephine openings of different dates—some more healed than others. . . .

Trephining, of course, is performed as one of the standard operations of modern surgery. It consists in taking a plate out of the bony dome of the skull. It is performed for various purposes. Remember that the skull is an unyielding casket for the brain—very useful because it protects perfectly this most vital of all structures. But the arrangement has its disadvantages. When disease occurs inside the skull—when, for instance, a tumor begins to grow—the vital brain substance is compressed and destroyed. The surgeon renders help in these circumstances by making an opening in the skull—trephining. This opening allows the contents to bulge and reduces the headache and other sufferings, preserves the intellect, and prolongs life. Sometimes through such openings it is possible to remove the tumor or loosen adhesions which are causing trouble.

This primitive operation of trephining represents one of the first upward steps we can discern in the development of scientific medicine.

Before that, all explanation of disease was magic. Devils had entered the sick man's body.

The cure for this was exorcism—driving the devils out by incantation. Ceremonies of exorcism—sometimes a ritual dance, sometimes a personal service of prayer, fast, and confession—were performed by the medicine man. . . .

The medicine man was especially selected. Usually he was marked out from birth. In Liberia twins are regarded as particularly gifted. Seventh sons, as is well known, are attuned to the whisperings of the infinite. And, of course, the seventh son of a seventh son is doubly dyed. . . .

Babies who come into the world feet first are adept at setting fractures and curing lumbago. Those who have fits, trances, convulsions, dreams, or nightmares are obviously the tabernacles of divine visitation.

The king touches for the king's evil. "The king's evil" was scrofula, which is tuberculosis of the lymph nodes of the neck. These nodes swell up, however, from many causes—simple tonsillitis, for instance—and after the acute infection is reduced, the swelling of the glands goes down. It was probably this type of the disease which responded to the magic of the royal touch, although even tuberculosis of the nodes subsides spontaneously. There is no necessity, therefore, to doubt that the touch often resulted in cures. . . .

The office for the ceremony of touching for the king's evil was included in the *Book of Common Prayer*. In connection with the ceremony the sovereign always gave the afflicted patient a coin, known as a touch piece. Usually it was specially coined, of bronze or silver or gold, of the value of an angel (ten shillings). Those now in existence in museums are usually pierced, for the patient wore the touch piece around the neck.

William III was openly contemptuous of the royal touch. "It is a silly superstition," he said. "Give the poor creatures some money and send them away." When forced into the position once of laying his hand on a rich man, he said: "God give you better health and more sense."

The house of Hanover carried the note of skepticism to its final point. George I declined to touch the child of an English gentleman and with great good humor referred him to the exiled Stuart pretender, who indeed was sought after all his life for this purpose and who touched frequently. . . .

So much for ancient and relatively modern examples of exorcism.

Another branch of magic, which may be called witchcraft, supposes that it is possible for one person to "send" disease upon another.

A simple form of witchcraft lies in the theory of the effigy. If a savage makes an effigy of a man, he somehow controls that man's mana. All primitive people object violently to being photographed or painted. Magical law says that their images are themselves. An Ojibway medicine man will construct a wooden doll—an image of his petitioner's enemy—and run a needle into the eye or heart: then the enemy will go blind or die of heart pangs.

Any part of the body must be kept out of the hands of an enemy: hair, nail parings, even clothes or soil in which are bare footprints. For the enemy will use these in lieu of the body itself and work destruction. The Victorian Blacks burn an enemy's cast-off hair and cause fever. In Scotland up to sixty years ago to burn feces caused dysentery. . . .

Human beings may possess the power to confer disease and misfortune, as witness the evil eye.

Just as the treatment for demoniacal possession was exorcism, so the prevention of witchcraft was a charm.

To ward off the evil eye, raise the hand with the middle fingers closed.

Amulets, talismans, cryptic writings! There is the story of a youth at Oxford who went out into the fields and sat beneath a tree to study. Idly he traced some Greek letters upon a sheet of paper—one lovely phrase that caught his fancy. Idly he fell asleep, and when he woke, the twilight was gray about him. A young girl—a country lass—had been watching him and shyly asked for the paper on which the Greek words were written. He gave it to her and, gathering up his books, strolled back to his study. And time went on and he left Oxford. He succeeded in his work and was made a judge. One day he was presiding at Oxford and they brought before him a miserable old woman, accused of being a witch. The countryfolk said she charmed the cattle with a paper on which was cabalistic writing. The judge asked to see it, and they passed it up to him. Dimly the old man seemed to remember something familiar. Then suddenly it came to him: the so potent charm was that chorus ending from Euripides which he had scribbled and left beneath the gray towers of Oxford long ago when all the world was young.

Of other charms and healing ways:

Iron is widely regarded as having specially valuable properties . . .

Mad stones are still used for the bite of a mad dog. The milpreve is a blue stone supposed to be concentrated crystallized snake venom. In the west of England milpreve is hung around the necks of cattle to prevent the bites of adders. If one gets a stone from the stomach or gall bladder of an animal (a bezoar stone), it is naturally more powerful than any ordinary stone.

Constriction cures are everywhere practiced. Rheumatism rings are an example. In Derbyshire a red thread is tied around the neck to prevent goiter. . . .

"Everybody has heard of cures by saliva. . . . Warts, contracted sinews, wounds, sores, and skin rashes in general are to this day treated by the application of saliva, that secreted in the morning before breakfast being considered the most efficacious. . . .

"When a Dyak of Borneo is seized with vomiting and sweating he thinks that an unfriendly ancestral spirit has chased out his soul and has taken its place. So he sends for a wise woman . . . and after she has identified the intruding spirit . . . an effigy is molded from the ashes of the hearth, and . . . the wise woman moves it seven times up and down before the patient. Then the patient spits upon the image, and the disease is thereby transferred to the spirit via his effigy." (Dan McKenzie: *The Infancy of Medicine*.)

. . . "Frog in the throat" is a disease of Cheshire which is treated by holding the head of a frog in the child's mouth for a few moments; the disease passes into the animal.

The orthodox method of curing abdominal cramps is to hold a live animal on the belly. For gripes, according to Marcellus (A.D. 300), a live duck was applied to the abdomen, and the pains passed into the duck, "to whom they prove fatal."

Goiter can be transferred to a corpse, by having the hand of the corpse (especially of a young child or a suicide) touch the enlarged thyroid nine times. A young woman was led on the scaffold of Old Bailey in order to get rid of a wen by having it touched by the hand of the man just executed. In Northampton patients used to congregate around the gallows in order to receive the "dead stroke." The fee went to the hangman. . . .

The Quixos Indians treat illness by whipping the patient with nettles.

Compared with such things, trephining was a sheer intellectual leap.

The devil was still the cause of the disease. But they had located the devil. The symptoms of epilepsy or headache or insanity were those belonging to the head. The devil who caused this sort of mischief was in the skull. Therefore, make a hole there to drive him out.

It was the beginning of reason.

2. The Beginnings of Physiology—William Harvey

In our preface we made the distinction between the medicine man and the modern physician, who depends on scientific methods of diagnosis and treatment. The man who first initiated such methods, and who is thus rightfully called the Father of Medicine, was a Greek named Hippocrates who lived about the year 400 B.C. It was Hippocrates who first divorced medicine from soothsaying and superstition, who painstakingly recorded symptoms in what we now call clinical case histories, and who, in his attempt to differentiate between the various diseases, founded the sciences of diagnosis and prognosis. He was the apostle of accuracy and common sense. Speaking of the so-called "sacred disease," he said, "It appears to me to be nowise more divine nor more sacred than other diseases, but has a natural cause from which it originates like other affections." Above all, he introduced the note of humanity into medicine. His aim was to alleviate human suffering. The high moral code by which he lived is expressed in our first selection, the Hippocratic Oath.

The members of the school which Hippocrates founded were enlightened men who used such modern techniques as clinical lectures and bedside instruction of their pupils. Before the Dark Ages cast their pall on all science, the spirit of Hippocrates and his followers, though often degraded, was not entirely lost. A great medical school was founded at Alexandria, where physicians made the first attempts to understand human anatomy and physiology. The Romans, although their methods were crude, emphasized the importance of sanitation, of hospitals, and of public health. Their greatest physician, Galen of Pergamum, who lived in the second century A.D., left a vast store of writings about the human body, based on original observation. Unfortunately these writings, while occasionally accurate, were usually grossly in error. It was one of the tragedies of the fifteen hundred years that followed that Galen's observations were considered sacrosanct to such an extent that the slightest deviation from his gospel was punished by ostracism and even torture and death.

Not until the Renaissance was this blind belief in tradition overthrown. One of the first to question Galen's omniscience was that overpowering genius Leonardo da Vinci. His magnificent drawings of the heart, lungs, and blood vessels were based on actual observation, but he failed to publish his work, and his influence on medicine was small. It remained for Andreas Vesalius, a native of Brussels who later journeyed to Padua in Italy, to publish a masterpiece entitled *On the Fabric of the Human Body* which was to revolutionize the study of human anatomy. From the very beginning of his studies, Vesalius had a passion for dissection. He once went to the length of stealing the skeleton of a criminal who had been left hanging on the gallows. His book contained numerous errors, but it was so far superior to anything that had previously appeared that it became one of the great landmarks in the history of medicine.

Vesalius made Padua a famous center of medical learning. As Logan Clendening tells us, he was the first in a line of noted anatomists whose work inspired another great physician, the Englishman William Harvey, to discover the circulation of the blood.

Sometime during the last years of the sixteenth century (1599 in all probability), about the time Shakespeare's plays were making such a furore in London, a swarthy, bellicose young Englishman named William Harvey entered the ancient city of Padua and prepared to enroll himself as a student in the university.

He had graduated in 1597 from Caius College, Cambridge, and had decided to complete his medical education at the Italian university, made famous for its anatomy by Vesalius. Caius College (which is still pronounced "Keyes" College, its founder being Sir John Keyes, whose name Latinized is spelled "Caius") directed his bent strongly toward anatomy, as Sir John was the first to introduce the study of practical anatomy into England.

Young Harvey had wandered down to Italy. . . . It was a leisurely journey through the Low Countries, down the Rhine, through Switzerland perhaps, and over the Alps.

Everywhere he went, Harvey heard of the fame of the professor of anatomy at Padua, Fabricius of Aquapendente. Fabricius had been a pupil of the great Fallopius, who, in turn, had been a pupil of Vesalius himself, so that the succession was authentic. Fabricius had built a magnificent anatomical theater at Padua. It was arranged with seats in tiers around the little space in the center where the body under dissection lay upon a table. This allowed everyone to obtain a seat with a good view of the subject. The theater is still preserved exactly as it must have been in those days when William Harvey sat on the benches.

Harvey acquitted himself creditably at Padua. He was elected councilor of the English nation (that is, the English students). . . . As one enters the courtyard of the medical school of the university today, where medical students are loitering in little groups, discussing the human body, which will ever remain their most fascinating topic, the first thing that strikes the American visitor is the blaze of color from the stemmata, or coats of arms, of former students and professors placed upon the wall. Proper search will uncover the one belonging to "Gulielmus Harveus, Anglus" (William Harvey, the Englishman).

Early in his career as medical student at Padua, Harvey began to hear discussed the mooted question of the anatomy of the heart and blood vessels. . . .

The popular idea is that Harvey discovered the fact that the blood moves, propelled by the heart. But that is not an exact statement of his contribution. What he did was to prove that the blood moved *in a circle*, and he demonstrated the exact path over which it moved.

People have written that because Shakespeare makes Brutus say to his wife (in the play of *Julius Caesar*):

> "You are . . .
> As dear to me as are the ruddy drops
> That visit my sad heart,"

Shakespeare might claim priority in being the discoverer of the circulation of the blood. But this is not the circulation of the blood. This is only the motion of the blood. . . .

Young William Harvey was, from the outset of his medical studies, fascinated by the problem of the heart and blood vessels. He must have been considerably mixed up by what he was taught.

Here was his teacher Fabricius, who had discovered that the veins had little valves in them—all through their courses. The valves are so placed that they obviously keep the blood from flowing out to the extremities, as Galen said it did. And yet Fabricius, with the refutation of that fact staring him in the face, got himself hopelessly intricated in a theory—he taught that the valves were in the veins to prevent the blood from flowing out to the extremities too rapidly: they allowed only as much as is needed to get there. . . .

When Harvey returned to England, in 1602, his mind was full of the perplexities of the problem. He settled in practice in London and was licensed by the College of Physicians.

In 1615 he was appointed Lumelian Lecturer on Anatomy at the Royal College of Surgeons. On April 16, 17, and 18, 1616, he gave his first course of lectures on the internal organs. It was quite a month for England. The next week—on April 23 William Shakespeare, a gent and a play actor, died at Stratford on Avon.

"After all, what can I learn from *dead* bodies?" The thought occurred to Harvey, the young professor. "The life, the movement of the blood, has gone out from them."

Here was a step forward from Vesalius. Galen had dissected dead animal bodies. Vesalius had improved knowledge by dissecting dead human bodies. Now Harvey wanted to see the inside of living bodies.

Of course he could not use living human bodies. But he began to use living animal bodies—snakes and fish at first.

He dissected out an artery and put a small ligature around it. Then he made a nick in it on the side toward the heart. At each heartbeat blood spurted out from the artery. Gradually less and less blood spurted. The heart flagged. "Why was that?" he asked. Wasn't it because no more blood came back to the heart? If Galen's theory were correct, the liver would manufacture blood, and a continuous supply would keep up.

To complete this experiment, he tied the large blood vessel coming from the heart in a snake and nicked an opening in it on the side away from the heart. No blood flowed. But in a few seconds the heart swelled to bursting with the engorgement of the blood which entered it from the lungs and other parts of the body. Finally all the animal's blood had accumulated in the heart.

Then he tied a constriction around a human arm. The veins swelled out and the little nodules, each of which marked the site of a valve in the vein, could be seen just as his teacher Fabricius so often demonstrated. But Harvey now went further. He milked the blood out of the veins toward the heart, starting exactly where a valve was located. Very rapidly the blood came up *from the extremity toward the heart* and filled the vein again.

Then he did something quite ingenious. He put his finger on a superficial vein in a man's arm, and with the other finger milked all the blood out of the vein toward the heart. Then he lifted the finger nearest the heart. No blood came into the vein. The valves held it back. Then he lifted the finger where he had originally compressed the vein. The blood filled the vein, coming up from the extremity toward the heart.

What had he proved by these experiments?

First, that blood flowed out from the heart in the arteries.

Second, that blood flowed toward the heart in the veins.

And, third, by inference, that all the blood in the body was constantly moving in a circle. From the left heart, out through the arteries, into the veins, back to the right heart.

Then came the question: How did it get from the right heart to the left heart? He proved that Galen and Vesalius were wrong about openings in the septum. They simply did not exist. There is no direct communication in normal hearts from the right to the left ventricle.

"Well, there is a plain path," said Harvey, just as Servetus had, "for the blood to travel—from the right ventricle out through the pulmonary artery to the lungs, through the lungs, emptying into the pulmonary vein, which returns the blood to the left side of the heart. There is a valve at the opening of the pulmonary artery which prevents the blood from returning to the heart once it enters the artery. There is only one place for the blood to go—through the lungs."

He stewed and thought and experimented and lectured on these ideas. . . . Then he made the great final experiment. It was conceived reasonably and logically.

"How much," he wondered to himself one day, "how much blood does the heart eject in one beat?"

"Not more than the size or contents of the ventricles," was the obvious answer.

"How often does the ventricle eject this amount?"

"Seventy-two times a minute" (that is, the rate of the pulse).
"All right, let us measure the size of a ventricle."

He killed a sheep and took out its heart. He poured water into
its ventricle. It held about two ounces. A man's is about the same.
Very well, then, if it beats seventy-two times a minute, it will
force out about three and a half pounds of blood in that time.

But now let us see how much blood there is in the body. He
tried it on a sheep, bled it of every drop—only four pounds. The
experiment was complete. If the heart continues to force out
blood at the rate of three and a half pounds an hour, and there
are only four pounds of blood in the body, there is not enough
new blood for the heart to work on; the blood *must* return to
the heart again.

It moves in a circle.

In 1628, there appeared the announcement of these experiments and a clear statement of the conclusion to which they led.
Exercitatio anatomica de motu cordis et sanguinis in animalibus
is the name of his book—*Anatomical Exercises on the Motion of
the Heart and Blood in Animals*—by William Harvey; printed
at Frankfurt. Only a few copies exist today.

It would be difficult to overestimate the influence of this
book. It did one of the most difficult things in the world—it
pulled men's minds out of a groove of thought. Even such an
original as Vesalius was in that groove.

Sober scholars have called it one of the greatest books that
ever were written. Certainly only the *Fabrica* of Vesalius chal-
lenges its right to be called the greatest of medical books.

Its importance lies first in the fact that a realization of the
circulation of the blood unifies one's conception of the functions
of the animal body.

All those functions depend upon a circulating fluid or medium
of exchange. The stomach and intestines digest food, and the
circulation of the blood carries this nutriment to the whole body.

The muscles and other organs throw their waste products into the blood stream, and the *circulation of the blood* carries them to the lungs and kidneys to be cast off. As the blood passes through the lungs, it picks up the necessary vital elements from the air to distribute to all parts.

Thus, you see, this conception opened the way for knowledge of the functions of the stomach, the liver, the lungs, the kidneys, and the muscles.

In surgery, too, its effect was fundamental. The first great problem of surgery is the control of hemorrhage. Whenever the surgeon cuts into the body, there is bleeding, and if he cannot control this, the patient will die and the operation might as well not have been performed. And no control of hemorrhage can be anything but bungling unless the mechanics of the circulation are understood.

In obstetrics, too—the knowledge of the method of the development of children—there came light. One of the great problems, a subject for debate before Harvey, was what the after-birth, that big, spongy red mass attached to the baby by a cord, actually did. In 1667 Walter Needham showed that it communicated with the mother's blood and furnished nourishment to the developing fetus.

Only secondary in importance to the actual proof of the circulation of the blood was the way Harvey demonstrated it. Not by theory or reason, but by experiment on animals. Forever after men were to be forced to go to the book of nature, not to authority, if they were to be sure of nature's ways. Everything he says and does is experimental, not mouthing.

"In fishes, also, if the blood vessels leading from the heart to the gills is cut open, the blood will be seen to spurt out when the heart contracts." Experiment on a living animal.

Or: "I once had a patient which convinced me of this truth." Observation of nature.

Or: "In a hen's egg I showed the first beginning of the chick like a little cloud, by putting the egg off which the shell was taken into water warm and clear, in the midst of which cloud there was a point of blood which did beat, so little, that when it was contracted it disappeared and vanished out of our sight, and in its dilation, showed itself red and small, as the point of a needle . . . it did represent a beating and the beginning of life." Experiment and observation combined.

The significance of this greatest discovery in the record of medical science became evident as time went on, but at first, although the work was widely read, it gained no adherents from any of the established anatomists of Europe. When recognition did come, it was from the younger men. . . .

There was, it must be acknowledged, one point in his doctrine which did not admit of clear demonstration in his own day and was a logical point of attack for critics. That was the query: *How does the blood get from the arteries to the veins?* It goes out from the left heart in the arteries, and back to the right heart in the veins, but no connections could be made out between the arteries and veins. Harvey admits this freely. "I have never succeeded in tracing any connection between the arteries and veins by a direct anastomosis of their orifices." He supposed the blood from the arteries flowed out into the tissue spaces and that the veins, opening with hungry mouths into the same spaces, drank it up.

As we know today, the connection is made by the capillaries —those minute thin-walled vessels which can be seen only by a microscope. But Harvey had no microscope.

In 1660, three years after Harvey's death, Marcello Malpighi with one of the early crude microscopes saw among the "so many marvels of nature spread before my eyes," when he placed the lung of a frog opposite his microscope lens and turned the instrument "against the horizontal sun," the blood cells passing from the small arteries through ever smaller but definite channels (the capillaries) to the widening slower stream of the veins.

By the middle of the seventeenth century the doctrine of the circulation of the blood was generally accepted. "He is the only man perhaps," wrote Mr. Hobbes, "that ever lived to see his doctrine established in his lifetime."

He was fifty when this, his most important book, was published.

After this, Harvey's life went on about thirty years. It was a period crowded with external incident but little inner fruitfulness. He went on divers journeys on the Continent; he was, at least partly, instrumental in saving the lives of some miserable old women in Lancashire, accused of being witches; he examined after death the body of the aged Thomas Parr—"old Parr"—who was said to have been a hundred and fifty-two at the time of his death; he accompanied his royal master, Charles I, to his wars, sat under a tree at the Battle of Edgehill, in charge of the two little princes, until it was time for him to dress the wounds of the soldiers. . . .

For many years he must have been a familiar figure in the streets of London—busy with his practice, with his lectures at the Royal College of Physicians. He was a small-statured, bad-tempered, choleric little man, 'tis said. Like most persons of sense, he did not suffer fools gladly, and favored many people with extremely short answers.

Among these must be reckoned that great philosopher . . . Lord Chancellor Bacon. Harvey attended him in a professional capacity. He would not allow him to be a great philosopher, his biographer Aubrey tells us. "He writes philosophy like a Lord Chancellor," he said, adding: "I have cured him."

He gave it as his mature opinion that man was but a great mischievous baboon.

"After his book on the circulation of the blood came out he

fell mightily in his practice and 'twas believed by the vulgar that he was crack brained. . . ."

He had a parrot which he thought was a male until it died. Then the "father of English midwifery" dissected it and found it was a female.

He had the pain of seeing his country in the toils of civil strife. Through it all he remained loyal to his king. He must often have met General Cromwell in his rounds, and we may imagine the contemptuous pride with which he strutted past him. Indeed, the Commonwealth troopers broke into his rooms in Whitehall once and destroyed many drawings and descriptions of experiments. But Dr. Harvey was too useful a man for the Protector, generous hater that he was, to put under any personal humiliation or inconvenience. He may, though we have no record of it, have been consulted about Mr. Milton's approaching blindness. It is not impossible that he was consulted by young Master Samuel Pepys for the symptoms which eventually turned out to be caused by those stones in the bladder which so interested Mr. Pepys all his life. It is very likely, since they were of the same political complexion, that he attended Richard Lovelace and Sir John Suckling.

So in this busy, fussy sort of existence he went on to his seventy-ninth year, when one morning he woke to find his tongue palsied. He made a sign to the apothecary who was sent for to bleed him from a vein under the tongue, but happily his misery was short and that night he died. "Lapt in lead" (in a mummy case of lead), he was laid to rest in Hempstead Church, Essex, June 26, 1657.

UNSEEN ENEMIES

Leeuwenhoek: First
of the Microbe Hunters

by Paul de Kruif

The work of Vesalius and Harvey broke the bonds which had shackled medicine for more than a thousand years. Now, at last, physicians felt free to observe, to experiment, to rely on their own experience and intelligence, instead of on the dicta of men long dead and better forgotten. As a result, discoveries about the human body followed thick and fast. Physicians dissected and studied. They observed in sickrooms and hospitals. They experimented with new methods of treatment. Yet their attempts to understand the fundamental reasons for the existence of disease ended only in bafflement.

All unknown to them and indeed also to himself, a cantankerous Dutchman who was a contemporary of Harvey had discovered the cause. Today, every well-educated person knows that most diseases are owing to tiny organisms, none of which can be seen with the naked eyes and some of which are so small that they cannot be detected even by the most powerful microscope. The study of sickness and the advancement of medicine have been in very large part the study of how these entities live and grow and how they can be controlled. Yet the first man who observed them was not a physician and knew nothing about how microbes caused illness.

Although, as far as we know, he had no interest in medicine, the work of the little Dutchman Leeuwenhoek is one

27

of the great foundation stones of the science. Two centuries were to elapse before his discoveries were to bear fruit. But thereafter the study of his "tiny living creatures" was to result in some of the most glorious pages in the history of medicine. Our section, *Unseen Enemies*, is devoted to some of the outstanding discoveries in this field.

––––––––––

Two hundred and fifty years ago* an obscure man named Leeuwenhoek looked for the first time into a mysterious new world peopled with a thousand different kinds of tiny beings, some ferocious and deadly, others friendly and useful, many of them more important to mankind than any continent or archipelago.

Leeuwenhoek, unsung and scarce remembered, is now almost as unknown as his strange little animals and plants were at the time he discovered them. This is the story of Leeuwenhoek, the first of the microbe hunters.

Today it is respectable to be a man of science. Those who go by the name of scientist form an important element of the population, their laboratories are in every city, their achievements are on the front pages of the newspapers, often before they are fully achieved. But take yourself back to Leeuwenhoek's day, two hundred and fifty years ago, and imagine yourself just through high school, getting ready to choose a career, wanting to know—

You have lately recovered from an attack of mumps, you ask your father what is the cause of mumps and he tells you a mumpish evil spirit has got into you. His theory may not impress you much, but you decide to make believe you believe him and not to wonder any more about what is mumps—because if you publicly don't believe him you are in for a beating and may even be turned out of the house. Your father is Authority.

*In 1926, when this selection was written.—Eds.

That was the world more than three hundred years ago, when Leeuwenhoek was born. It was a world where science (which only means trying to find truth by careful observation and clear thinking) was just learning to toddle on vague and wobbly legs. It was a world where Servetus was burned to death for daring to cut up and examine the body of a dead man, where Galileo was shut up for life for daring to prove that the earth moved around the sun.

Anton Leeuwenhoek was born in 1632 amid the blue windmills and low streets and high canals of Delft, in Holland. His family were burghers of an intensely respectable kind and I say intensely respectable because they were basketmakers and brewers, and brewers are respectable and highly honored in Holland. Leeuwenhoek's father died early and his mother sent him to school to learn to be a government official, but he left school at sixteen to be an apprentice in a dry-goods store in Amsterdam. That was his university. Think of a present-day scientist getting his training for experiment among bolts of gingham, listening to the tinkle of the bell on the cash drawer, being polite to an eternal succession of Dutch housewives who shopped with a penny-pinching dreadful exhaustiveness—but that was Leeuwenhoek's university for six years!

At the age of twenty-one he left the dry-goods store, went back to Delft, married, set up a dry-goods store of his own there. For twenty years after that very little is known about him, except that he had two wives (in succession) and several children, most of whom died, but there is no doubt that during this time he was appointed janitor of the city hall of Delft, and that he developed a most idiotic love for grinding lenses. He had heard that if you very carefully ground very little lenses out of clear glass, you would see things look much bigger than they appeared to the naked eye. . . . Little is known about him from twenty to forty, but there is no doubt that he passed in those days for an ignorant man. Just the same, you will see that his ignorance was a great help to him, for, cut off from all of the learned nonsense of his time, he had to trust to his own eyes, his own thoughts, his own judgment. And that was easy for him because there never was a more mulish man than this Anton Leeuwenhoek!

It would be great fun to look through a lens and see things bigger than your naked eye showed them to you! But *buy* lenses! Not Leeuwenhoek! There never was a more suspicious man. Buy lenses? He would make them himself! During these twenty years of his obscurity he went to spectacle makers and got the rudiments of lens grinding. He visited alchemists and apothecaries and put his nose into their secret ways of getting metals from ores, he began fumblingly to learn the craft of the gold- and silversmiths. He was a most pernickety man and was not satisfied with grinding lenses as good as those of the best lens grinder in Holland, they had to be better than the best, and then he still fussed over them for long hours. Next he mounted these lenses in little oblongs of copper or silver or gold, which he had extracted himself, over hot fires, among strange smells and fumes. Today searchers pay many dollars for a fine shining microscope, turn the screws, peer through it, make discoveries —without knowing anything about how it is built. But Leeuwenhoek—

Of course his neighbors thought he was a bit cracked, but Leeuwenhoek went on burning and blistering his hands. Working forgetful of his family and regardless of his friends, he bent solitary to subtle tasks in still nights. The good neighbors snickered, while that man found a way to make a tiny lens, less than one eighth of an inch across, so symmetrical, so perfect, that it showed little things to him with a fantastic clear enormousness. Yes, he was a very uncultured man, but he alone of all men in Holland knew how to make those lenses, and he said of his neighbors: "We must forgive them, seeing that they know no better."

Now this self-satisfied dry-goods dealer began to turn his lenses onto everything he could get hold of. He looked through them at the muscle fibers of a whale and the scales of his own skin. He went to the butcher shop and begged or bought ox eyes and was amazed at how prettily the crystalline lens of the eye of the ox is put together. He peered for hours at the build of the hairs of a sheep, of a beaver, of an elk, that were transformed from their fineness into great rough logs under his bit of glass. He delicately dissected the head of a fly; he stuck its brain on the fine needle of his microscope—how he admired the clear details of the marvelous big brain of that fly! He examined the cross sections of the wood of a dozen different trees and squinted at the seeds of plants. He grunted "Impossible!" when he first spied the outlandish large perfection of the sting of a flea and the legs of a louse. That man Leeuwenhoek was like a puppy who sniffs—with a totally impolite disregard of discrimination—at every object of the world around him!

There never was a less sure man than Leeuwenhoek. He looked at this bee's sting or that louse's leg again and again and again. He left his specimens sticking on the point of his strange microscope for months—in order to look at other things he made more microscopes till he had hundreds of them!—then he came back to those first specimens to correct his first mistakes. He never set down a word about anything he peeped at, he never made a drawing until hundreds of peeps showed him that, under given conditions, he would always see exactly the same thing. And then he was not sure! He said: "People who look for the first time through a microscope say now I see this and then I see that— and even a skilled observer can be fooled. On these observations I have spent more time than many will believe, but I have done them with joy, and I have taken no notice of those who have said why take so much trouble and what good is it?—but I do not write for such people but only for the philosophical!" He worked for twenty years that way, without an audience.

But at this time, in the middle of the seventeenth century, great things were astir in the world. Here and there in France and England and Italy rare men were thumbing their noses at almost everything that passed for knowledge. "We will no longer take Aristotle's say-so, nor the Pope's say-so," said these rebels. "We will trust only the perpetually repeated observations of our own eyes and the careful weighings of our scales; we will listen to the answers experiments give us and no other answers!" So in England a few of these revolutionists started a society called The Invisible College. It had to be invisible because that man Cromwell might have hung them for plotters and heretics if he had heard of the strange questions they were trying to settle. What experiments those solemn searchers made! Put a spider in a circle made of the powder of a unicorn's horn and that spider can't crawl out—so said the wisdom of that day. But these Invisible Collegians? One of them brought what was supposed to be powdered unicorn's horn and another came carrying a little spider in a bottle. The college crowded around under the light of high candles. Silence, then the hushed experiment, and here is their report of it: "A circle was made with the powder of unicorn's horn and a spider set in the middle of it, but immediately ran out."

Crude, you exclaim. Of course! But remember that one of the members of this college was Robert Boyle, founder of the science of chemistry, and another was Isaac Newton. Such was The Invisible College, and presently, when Charles II came to the throne, it rose from its depths as a sort of blind-pig scientific society to the dignity of the name of the Royal Society of England. And they were Anton Leeuwenhoek's first audience! There was one man in Delft who did not laugh at Anton Leeuwenhoek, and that was Regnier de Graaf, whom the Lords and Gentlemen of the Royal Society had made a corresponding member because he had written them of interesting things he had found in the human ovary. Already Leeuwenhoek was rather surly and suspected everybody, but he let De Graaf peep through those magic eyes of his, those little lenses whose equal did not exist in Europe or England or the whole world for that matter. What De Graaf saw through those microscopes made him ashamed of his own fame and he hurried to write to the Royal Society: "Get Anton Leeuwenhoek to write you telling of his discoveries."

And Leeuwenhoek answered the request of the Royal Society with all the confidence of an ignorant man who fails to realize the profound wisdom of the philosophers he addresses. It was a long letter, it rambled over every subject under the sun, it was written with a comical artlessness in the conversational Dutch that was the only language he knew. The title of that letter was: "A Specimen of some Observations made by a Microscope contrived by Mr. Leeuwenhoek, concerning Mold upon the Skin, Flesh, etc.; the Sting of a Bee, etc." The Royal Society was amazed, the sophisticated and learned gentlemen were amused—but principally the Royal Society was astounded by the marvelous things Leeuwenhoek told them he could see through his new lenses. The secretary of the Royal Society thanked Leeuwenhoek and told him he hoped his first communication would be followed by others. It was, by hundreds of others over a period of fifty years. They were talkative letters full of salty remarks about his ignorant neighbors, of exposures of charlatans and skilled explodings of superstitions, of chatter about his personal health—but sandwiched between paragraphs and pages of this homely stuff, in almost every letter, those Lords and Gentlemen of the Royal Society had the honor of reading immortal and gloriously accurate descriptions of the discoveries made by the magic eye of that janitor and shopkeeper. What discoveries!

When you look back at them, many of the fundamental discoveries of science seem so simple, too absurdly simple. How was it men groped and fumbled for so many thousands of years without seeing things that lay right under their noses? So with microbes. Now all the world has seen them cavorting on movie screens, many people of little learning have peeped at them swimming about under lenses of microscopes, the greenest medical student is able to show you the germs of I don't know how many diseases—what was so hard about seeing microbes for the first time?

But let us remember that when Leeuwenhoek was born there were no microscopes but only crude hand lenses that would hardly make a ten-cent piece look as large as a quarter. Through these—without his incessant grinding of his own marvelous lenses —that Dutchman might have looked till he grew old without discovering any creature smaller than a cheese mite. You have read that he made better and better lenses with the fanatical persistence of a lunatic; that he examined everything, the most intimate things and the most shocking things, with the silly curiosity of a puppy. Yes, and all this squinting at bee stings and mustache hairs and what not was needful to prepare him for that sudden day when he looked through his toy of a gold-mounted lens at a fraction of a small drop of clear rain water to discover—

Leeuwenhoek was a maniac observer, and who but such a strange man would have thought to turn his lens on clear, pure water, just come down from the sky? What could there be in water but just—water? You can imagine his daughter Maria—she was nineteen and she took such care of her slightly insane father! —watching him take a little tube of glass, heat it red-hot in a flame, draw it out to the thinness of a hair. . . . Maria was devoted to her father—let any of those stupid neighbors dare to snicker at him—but what in the world was he up to now, with that hair-fine glass pipe?

You can see her watch that absent-minded, wide-eyed man break the tube into little pieces, go out into the garden to bend over an earthen pot kept there to measure the fall of the rain. He bends over that pot. He goes back into his study. He sticks the little glass pipe onto the needle of his microscope. . . .

What can that dear silly father be up to? He squints through his lens. He mutters guttural words under his breath. . . . Then, suddenly, the excited voice of Leeuwenhoek: "Come here! Hurry! There are little animals in this rain water. . . . They swim! They play around! They are a thousand times smaller than any creatures we can see with our eyes alone. . . . Look! See what I have discovered!"

Leeuwenhoek's day of days had come. Alexander had gone to India and discovered huge elephants that no Greek had ever seen before—but those elephants were as commonplace to Hindus as horses were to Alexander. Caesar had gone to England and come upon savages that opened his eyes with wonder—but these Britons were as ordinary to each other as Roman centurions were to Caesar. Balboa? What were his proud feelings as he looked for the first time at the Pacific? Just the same that ocean was as ordinary to a Central American Indian as the Mediterranean was to Balboa. But Leeuwenhoek? This janitor of Delft had stolen upon and peeped into a fantastic sub-visible world of little things, creatures that had lived, had bred, had battled, had died, completely hidden from and unknown to all men from the beginning of time. Beasts these were of a kind that ravaged and annihilated whole races of men ten million times larger than they were themselves. Beings these were, more terrible than fire-spitting dragons or hydra-headed monsters. They were silent assassins that murdered babes in warm cradles and kings in sheltered places. It was this invisible, insignificant, but implacable —and sometimes friendly—world that Leeuwenhoek had looked into for the first time of all men of all countries.

This was Leeuwenhoek's day of days. . . .

That man was so unashamed of his admirations and his surprises at a nature full of startling events and impossible things. How I wish I could take myself back, could bring you back, to that innocent time when men were just beginning to disbelieve in miracles and only starting to find still more miraculous facts. How marvelous it would be to step into that simple Dutchman's shoes, to be inside his brain and body, to feel his excitement—it is almost nausea!—at his first peep at those cavorting "wretched beasties."

That was what he called them, and, as I have told you, this Leeuwenhoek was an unsure man. Those animals were too tremendously small to be sure, they were too strange to be true. So he looked again, till his hands were cramped with holding his microscope and his eyes full of that smarting water that comes from too-long looking. But he was right! Here they were again, not one kind of little creature, but here was another, larger than the first, "moving about very nimbly because they were furnished with divers incredibly thin feet." Wait! Here is a third kind—and a fourth, so tiny I can't make out his shape. But he is alive! He goes about, dashing over great distances in this world of his water drop in the little tube. . . . What nimble creatures!

"They stop, they stand still as 'twere upon a point, and then turn themselves round with that swiftness, as we see a top turn round, the circumference they make being no bigger than that of a fine grain of sand." So wrote Leeuwenhoek.

For all this seemingly impractical sniffing about, Leeuwenhoek was a hardheaded man. He hardly ever spun theories, he was a fiend for measuring things. Only how could you make a measuring stick for anything so small as these little beasts? He wrinkled his low forehead: "How large really is this last and smallest of the little beasts?" He poked about in the cobwebbed corners of his memory among the thousand other things he had studied with you can't imagine what thoroughness; he made calculations: "This last kind of animal is a thousand times smaller than the eye of a large louse!" That was an accurate man. For we know now that the eye of one full-grown louse is no larger nor smaller than the eyes of ten thousand of his brother and sister lice.

But where did these outlandish little inhabitants of the rain water come from? Had they come down from the sky? Had they crawled invisibly over the side of the pot from the ground? Or had they been created out of nothing by a God full of whims? Leeuwenhoek believed in God as piously as any seventeenth-century Dutchman. He always referred to God as the Maker of the Great All. He not only believed in God but he admired Him intensely—what a Being to know how to fashion bees' wings so prettily! But then Leeuwenhoek was a materialist, too. His good sense told him that life comes from life. His simple belief told him that God had invented all living things in six days, and, having set the machinery going, sat back to reward good observers and punish guessers and bluffers. He stopped speculating about improbable gentle rains of little animals from heaven. Certainly God couldn't brew those animals in the rainwater pot out of nothing! But wait . . . Maybe? Well, there was only one way to find out where they came from. "I will experiment!" he muttered.

He washed out a wineglass very clean, he dried it, he held it under the spout of his eaves trough, he took a wee drop in one of his hair-fine tubes. Under his lens it went. . . . Yes! They were there, a few of those beasts, swimming about. . . . "They are present even in very fresh rain water!" But then, that really proved nothing, they might live in the eaves trough and be washed down by the water. . . .

Then he took a big porcelain dish, "glazed blue within," he washed it clean, out into the rain he went with it and put it on top of a big box so that the falling raindrops would splash no mud into the dish. The first water he threw out to clean it still more thoroughly. Then intently he collected the next bit in one of his slender pipes. Into his study he went with it. . . .

"I have proved it! This water has not a single little creature in it! They do not come down from the sky!"

But he kept that water; hour after hour, day after day he squinted at it—and on the fourth day he saw those wee beasts beginning to appear in the water along with bits of dust and little flecks of thread and lint. His new beasties were marvelous but they were not enough for him, he was always poking into everything, trying to see more closely, trying to find reasons. Why is the sharp taste of pepper? That was what he asked himself one day, and he guessed: "There must be little points on the particles of pepper and these points jab the tongue when you eat pepper. . . ."

But are there such little points? He fussed with dry pepper. He sneezed. He sweat, but he couldn't get the grains of pepper small enough to put under his lens. So, to soften it, he put it to soak for several weeks in water. Then with fine needles he pried the almost invisible specks of the pepper apart, and sucked them up in a little drop of water into one of his hair-fine glass tubes. He looked—

Here was something to make even this determined man scatterbrained. He forgot about possible sharp points on the pepper. With the interest of an intent little boy he watched the antics of "an incredible number of little animals, of various sorts, which move very prettily, which tumble about and sidewise, this way and that!"

So it was that Leeuwenhoek stumbled on a magnificent way to grow his new little animals.

And now to write all this to the great men off there in London! Artlessly he described his own astonishment to them. Long page after page in a superbly neat handwriting with little common words he told them that you could put a million of these little animals into a coarse grain of sand and that one drop of his pepper water, where they grew and multiplied so well, held more than two million seven hundred thousand of them. . . .

This letter was translated into English. It was read before the learned skeptics—who no longer believed in the magic virtues of unicorns' horns—and it bowled the learned body over! What! The Dutchman said he had discovered beasts so small that you could put as many of them into one little drop of water as there were people in his native country? Nonsense! The cheese mite was absolutely and without doubt the smallest creature God had created.

But a few of the members did not scoff. This Leeuwenhoek was a confoundedly accurate man: everything he had ever written to them they had found to be true. . . . So a letter went back to the scientific janitor, begging him to write them in detail the way he had made his microscope, and his method of observing.

That upset Leeuwenhoek. It didn't matter that these stupid oafs of Delft laughed at him—but the Royal Society? He had thought *they* were philosophers! He replied to them in a long letter. He explained his calculations (and modern microbe hunters with all of their apparatus make only slightly more accurate ones!), he wrote these calculations out, divisions, multiplications, additions, until his letter looked like a child's exercise in arithmetic. He finished by saying that many people of Delft had seen—with applause!—these strange new animals under his lens. He would send them affidavits from prominent citizens of

Delft—two men of God, one notary public, and eight other persons worthy to be believed. But he wouldn't tell them how he made his microscopes.

So the Royal Society commissioned Robert Hooke and Nehemiah Grew to build the very best microscopes, and brew pepper water from the finest quality of black pepper. And on the 15th of November, 1677, Hooke came carrying his microscope to the meeting—agog—for Anton Leeuwenhoek had not lied. Here they were, those enchanted beasts! The members rose from their seats and crowded round the microscope. They peered, they exclaimed: this man must be a wizard observer! That was a proud day for Leeuwenhoek. And a little later the Royal Society made him a Fellow, sending him a gorgeous diploma of membership in a silver case with the coat of arms of the Society on the cover. "I will serve you faithfully during the rest of my life," he wrote them. And he was as good as his word, for he mailed them those conversational mixtures of gossip and science till he died at the age of ninety. But send them a microscope? Very sorry, but that was impossible to do, while he lived. The Royal Society went so far as to dispatch Dr. Molyneux to make a report on this janitor-discoverer of the invisible. Molyneux offered Leeuwenhoek a fine price for one of his microscopes—surely he could spare one? —for there were hundreds of them in cabinets that lined his study. But no!

Those little animals were everywhere! He told the Royal Society of finding swarms of those sub-visible beings in his mouth—of all places. "Although I am now fifty years old," he wrote, "I have uncommonly well-preserved teeth, because it is my custom every morning to rub my teeth very hard with salt, and after cleaning my large teeth with a quill, to rub them vigorously with a cloth. . . ." But there still were little bits of white stuff between his teeth when he looked at them with a magnifying mirror. . . . What was this white stuff made of?

From his teeth he scraped a bit of this stuff, mixed it with pure rain water, stuck it in a little tube on to the needle of his microscope, closed the door of his study—

What was this that rose from the gray dimness of his lens into clear distinctness as he brought the tube into the focus? Here was an unbelievably tiny creature, leaping about in the water of the tube "like the fish called a pike." There was a second kind that swam forward a little way, then whirled about suddenly, then tumbled over itself in pretty somersaults. There were some beings that moved sluggishly and looked like wee bent sticks, nothing more, but that Dutchman squinted at them till his eyes were red-rimmed—and they moved, they were alive, no doubt of it! There was a menagerie in his mouth! There were creatures shaped like flexible rods that went to and fro with the stately carriage of bishops in procession, there were spirals that whirled through the water like violently animated cork-screws. . . .

You may wonder that Leeuwenhoek nowhere in any of those hundreds of letters makes any mention of the harm these myste-rious new little animals might do to men. He had come upon them in drinking water, spied upon them in the mouth; as the years went by he discovered them in the intestines of frogs and horses, and even in his own discharges; in swarms he found them on those rare occasions when, as he says, "he was troubled with a looseness." But not for a moment did he guess that his trouble was caused by those little beasts.

The years went by. He tended his little dry-goods store, he saw to it the city hall of Delft was properly swept out, he grew more and more crusty and suspicious, he looked longer and longer hours through his hundreds of microscopes, he made a hundred amazing discoveries. In the tail of a little fish stuck head first into a glass tube he saw for the first time of all men the capil-lary blood vessels through which blood goes from the arteries to the veins—so he completed the Englishman Harvey's discovery of the circulation of the blood.

He wrote to the Royal Society: "When I have supped too heavily of an evening, I drink in the morning a large number of cups of coffee, and that as hot as I can drink it, so that the sweat breaks out on me."

That hot-coffee drinking led him to another curious fact about the little animals. Years after his discovery of the microbes in his mouth one morning he looked once more at the stuff between his teeth. What was this? There was not a single little animal to be found. Or there were no living animals rather, for he thought he could make out the bodies of myriads of dead ones—and maybe one or two that moved feebly, as if they were sick. "Blessed saints!" he growled: "I hope some great Lord of the Royal Society doesn't try to find those creatures in his mouth, and fail, and then deny my observations. . . ."

But look here! He had been drinking coffee, so hot it had blistered his lips almost. He had looked for the little animals in the white stuff from between his front teeth. It was just after the coffee he had looked there. Well?

With the help of a magnifying mirror he went at his back teeth. Presto! "With great surprise I saw an incredibly large number of little animals, and in such an unbelievable quantity of the aforementioned stuff, that it is not to be conceived of by those who have not seen it with their own eyes." Then he made delicate experiments in tubes, heating the water with its tiny population to a temperature a little warmer than that of a hot bath. In a moment the creatures stopped their agile runnings to and fro. He cooled the water. They did not come back to life—so! It was that hot coffee that had killed the beasties in his front teeth!

He passed eighty, and his teeth came loose as they had to even in his strong body; he didn't complain at the inexorable arrival of the winter of his life, but he jerked out that old tooth and turned his lens onto the little creatures he found within that hollow root. Why shouldn't he study them once more? There might be some little detail he had missed those hundred other times! Friends came to him at eighty-five and told him to take it easy and leave his studies. He wrinkled his brow and opened wide his still-bright eyes. "The fruits that ripen in autumn last the longest!" he told them—he called eighty-five the autumn of his life!

That was the first of the microbe hunters. In 1723, when he was ninety-one years old and on his deathbed, he sent for his friend Hoogvliet. He could not lift his hand. His once-glowing eyes were rheumy and their lids were beginning to stick fast with the cement of death. He mumbled: "Hoogvliet, my friend, be so good as to have those two letters on the table translated into Latin. . . . Send them to London to the Royal Society. . . ."

So he kept his promise made fifty years before, and Hoogvliet wrote, along with those last letters: "I send you, learned sirs, this last gift of my dying friend, hoping that his final word will be agreeable to you."

So he passed, this first of the microbe hunters. You will read of Pasteur who had a thousand times his imagination, of Robert Koch who did much more immediate apparent good in lifting the torments that microbes bring to men—these and all the others have much more fame today. But not one of them has been so completely honest, so appallingly accurate as this Dutch janitor, and all of them could take lessons from his splendid common sense.

A Pesthouse in Vienna

by Morton Thompson

It is perhaps surprising that so many years were to elapse between Leeuwenhoek's first observation of microbes and the discovery of their relationship to disease. There were numerous clues, but it took the genius of Pasteur and Koch to appreciate their significance. One such clue was contained in a paper in which John Snow, an English physician, proved that an epidemic of cholera that occurred in London in 1824 was caused by the drinking water of the Broad Street pump. Why was this water different from others? What caused the contamination? He did not know, but he was sure that sanitary measures would put an end to the epidemic, and so it proved.

Another clue was discovered in 1846 by Ignaz Semmelweis, who showed that puerperal fever, which was killing thousands of women in lying-in hospitals all over the world, was caused by the putrefaction on the hands of physicians who came to their patients directly from dissecting rooms where they had handled diseased bodies. He proved that clean hands could not carry the disease, but he did not probe deeply enough. If he had been able to connect his discovery with the fact that the putrefaction was caused by microbes, his contribution to medicine would have been enormously more important.

Semmelweis was nevertheless one of the great discoverers in medicine as well as one of its tragic martyrs. In the selection that follows we first see him as a young assistant in one of the wards of the lying-in hospital in Vienna. We follow him to the point where his discovery is accepted by

progressive physicians in his own country. Yet that is not
the entire story. In many quarters his work was greeted
with ridicule and abuse. Abnormally sensitive, almost to the
point of insanity, he abandoned one position after another.
He died from an infected finger, caused by the blood poisoning which he had proved to be identical with puerperal
fever. Not until the acceptance of Lister's antiseptic methods, described in a later section, were the ideas of Semmelweis universally adopted.

―――――――

For an instant, as he walked with Director Klein on his first day
as provisional assistant, in that silent, purposeful march, both in
step, faces grave, the eyes of the patients following respectfully,
Ignaz Philipp Semmelweis felt pride full force. His exultance was
brief. It was succeeded by embarrassment. He glanced to either
side covertly. He had almost strutted. No one had noticed. He
contemplated himself with disgust. Klein stopped at a bedside.

"I was noticing the sheets, sir director. On some of the beds
they are changed as often as once a week. And yet—"

"On the expenses of this division as a whole and in the matter
of laundry charges in particular my budget has been precisely
established. I may say that in all my career here the yearly bills
have hardly varied more than a few groschen. It is unfortunate
that they vary even that much."

"With respect, sir director, because of the discharge, the
natural staining, some of them, in fact, are very dirty—"

"They betray the normal consequences of hospital use. Their
care conforms to the restrictions of their part in the budget.
Naturally we do not expect that anyone should contemplate
altering the budget in the slightest particular."

"I regret having mentioned the matter, sir director—"

"It is of no consequence. That is how one learns. I want you
to feel free to come to me at any time between one o'clock in
the afternoon and three-thirty to discuss any matter that puzzles

you. In that way I shall feel you completely understand what it is I desire here. Punctuality, order, regularity, attention to the smallest detail—that is how one gets on, Dr. Semmelweis."

It was true, Ignaz Philipp reflected, that the First Division had a name for precision, for being well kept, for being administered to near perfection.

"I shall try to be a credit to you, sir director," he said. . . .

Markussovsky was sleeping heavily when Ignaz Philipp rose next morning. He dressed, he let himself out quietly. He walked briskly to the university. As he expected, Kolletschka was already in the dissecting room.

"Good morning, sir." Ignaz Philipp looked about the room.

"How much sleep are you getting lately?"

Ignaz Philipp pointed to a nearby cadaver.

"Not so much as him."

"Still, you are young. When you're old as I am there will still be plenty of time for work."

"They keep dying, sir. They keep on dying."

"I don't think we will ever find the reason here."

"I know. We keep turning the same findings over and over. But the secret must be here. There is no other place to look for it."

"We've examined so many women dead of childbed fever, Ignaz."

"I can't help it, sir. There's no place else to look. And always— perhaps the next one will give up the secret. Perhaps we're over- looking something. Perhaps if we do enough post-mortems we will find it. And it will be something very simple. Something, perhaps, we have been looking at all the time."

"It doesn't do any harm to look, certainly. You're learning a lot of gynecology, that's certain."

"That's right." He moved to a table and looked at the body.

"The same sort of fluid in the thorax—"

Kolletschka nodded sadly.

"A milky, putrid lymph in the lungs—pus around the ovaries—inflammation in the uterus—clots—some gangrene—the peritoneum inflamed—"

"Always, always the same—"

"Blisters of pus and foul-smelling fluid under the skin—"

"Well, we'll keep on hunting, you and I, as long as you please. You come here any time, Ignaz. I'll always be glad to help."

"You have, sir. You always have."

As he left the anatomy room and walked hastily to duty in the First Division, Ignaz Philipp marveled, as always, at Kolletschka's patience, his quietness, his warmth, and his affection. He thought with awe of his good fortune in such a friend.

He made his first discovery. He discovered from his statistics that during six years three times as many women died in the First Division as in the adjoining Second Division. He looked up from his papers. A faint hope pulsed in him. His heart beat faster.

On the twenty-seventh of February, 1846, obeying almost overwhelming faculty pressure, Klein reluctantly appointed him first assistant. Now, if it was possible, he worked harder than before. There were still theories to explore. There was no lack of learned theories. There was no lack of authorities. One after the other his research rejected such verdicts as summer heat and winter cold, the pestilential nature of the timbers and mortar, of the very building which enclosed the maternity hospital. All these things to which childbed fever was learnedly ascribed were common to both divisions. But the First Division's death rate continued invariably higher, and day by day the women continued to sicken, to cry out, to implore him, and to die.

Spring came late that year, winter lingered, at Graz travelers groaned about high snow in the Alpine passes. Ignaz Philipp and

Markussovsky skirted the high Alps, the stagecoach rumbled southward toward Trieste. For a day they sat quietly. They ignored their fellow passengers. Always they gazed at the changing landscape, sometimes seeing it, sometimes staring blindly.

On the morning of the second day Ignaz Philipp said abruptly, "What I am looking for is in the First Division and nowhere else."

His tone was final. His mind was calm and assured. The last doubts had left him.

The last few days of vacation they lay on the warm sands of Lido near Venice, simply resting, musing at a blue sky, a galloping of dappled clouds, content to wait for sunset.

It was over at last.

On March 20 he and Markussovsky arrived in Vienna. They stepped from the stagecoach from warm, golden spring into Austria's bitter winter. The next morning Ignaz Philipp reported for duty in the First Division. He was first assistant again.

"Well," said Klein, "this time I shall have perhaps your undivided attention."

"I have always tried to give you that, sir professor."

"Your comments are not necessary. Did you enjoy Venice? . . . Fine. . . . are you rested? . . . Splendid. . . . That will be all."

Ignaz Philipp walked to the door of the office.

"By the way, what was it Kolletschka was working on when you left?"

"He was experimenting with a stain he had developed for tissue mounted on microscopic slides—that and some work on lung tissue."

"I see. Perhaps that's what made him careless. One should devote all one's energies in that to which one is assigned. One hopes you profit from the lesson."

Cold, bitter cold clamped heavily on Ignaz Philipp's heart. He stared at Klein. His pulse pounded. He held his breath.

"What"—he licked his lips—"what's the matter with Kolletschka?"

"He's dead. Didn't anyone tell you? Died on the thirteenth of March. Cadaveric poisoning. Student pricked his finger while they were dissecting a corpse in class. We have a new provisional assistant. His name is Fleischer. See that he works. You may go."

He made his rounds mechanically. He led the students through the wards. He inspected the journal. Kolletschka was dead. He could think of nothing else. Jakob Kolletschka, aged forty-three, a true man, a friend, decent, gentle Kolletschka. He shut the journal. He walked from the First Division into the Second.

"What has happened, Bartsch? What happened to Kolletschka?"

"I'm sorry, Semmelweis. I knew it was going to be terrible for you. . . ."

"Why didn't you write? Why didn't someone tell me?"

"Professor Skoda said no. Ah, man, you were enjoying yourself—what good would it have done?"

"Tell me, Bartsch. Tell me what happened."

"It happened in class. He and a student were demonstrating visceral anatomy. The student was incising. He was clumsy and Kolletschka moved his hand to help him. The student nicked the end of his finger."

"And that's all?"

"It bled a little. It was a small nick, nothing much. Kolletschka went on with the lesson. You and I have had such nicks. But the next day he fell ill. He got worse. He was dead within the week. Cadaveric poisoning."

Bartsch looked down. Through the minds of both men rasped the refrain of agony in which men died of cadaveric poisoning.

"I thank you, Bartsch." Gentle Jakob. Gentle Jakob suffering. "I'm sorry, Semmelweis. I know you were friends. . . ."

"Thank you . . ." Jakob screaming, Jakob dead, Jakob dying. He finished his duties that day in almost complete silence. He saw the faces of the sick and the agonized. But often the face of Jakob was on the pillow. And often the voice was Kolletschka's.

The next day he rose early and went to the dissecting rooms. He worked alone. Kolletschka was gone. That night with Rokitansky, Hebra, Skoda, he bowed in silence before Frau Kolletschka.

Scrupulously he resumed where he had left off almost a month before. He dissected. He reported at the clinic. He worked harder than before. Each case became his own case, to each woman he fought to give some solace. He looked at them, row after row, each mattress freighted with its weight of misery and fear, and his heart surrendered to them utterly.

They had no money. They were sick. There was no place else for them to go. And each knew she was in a place of deadly peril. Each knew the bed might be her deathbed. Their eyes begged reassurance. They pleaded humbly to be healed, not to die, to have their babies and be released. They woke in fear and they bore in fear and they slept in fear. And that is how they died.

The killing went on. . . .

In the first ten days following his return to duty the death rate from puerperal fever which had subsided to an incredible 1.92 per cent rose abruptly to 3.60 per cent. He redoubled his dissecting. He rushed back to the wards and flogged himself to greater effort. The women screamed, they looked at him, imploring, he smiled a set smile, his eyes ached with pity, his hands detected the inevitable even as his voice tried to assure them. At the end of April the death rate had risen to 18.27 per cent. He set the figure in his records carefully.

He went to see Skoda . . . Perhaps there was something he could say, some word, which would remain with Skoda, which might inflame that great man so that he would pick up the problem.

"I've seen the latest figures," Skoda said without preamble.

Ignaz Philipp shook his head.

"Yes, sir. They're rising. . . ."

"Be careful, my boy. He may be using his peculiar bookkeeping to get rid of you. You go away—the figures go down. You come back—the death rate mounts. Keep your counsel. Don't be rash. . . . And now tell me! What is the latest? What have you found?"

"I will tell you. I will tell you an old story. Tomorrow it will be new. But there will be no change. You are at the hospital. You will admit a healthy woman. A sound, fine woman. This creature of God will come to you in the glory of health, groveling with fear. And you will tell her not to fear. You will use all your art. And she will have her child. And while you look at her, it will strike. There is, incredibly, a fever. There is vomiting. There is diarrhea. There is crunching pain. And now it is all over. In three days this healthy, praying woman is a burning, unrecognizable, insane corruption. And you will watch, helpless. And now she is gone. And we open her up. And we find—"

"Lymphangitis, phlebitis, bilateral pleuritis, pericarditis, peritonitis, meningitis, metastases. . . ."

"Yes, sir."

"But you keep on trying."

"There's that one clue—that higher rate in the First Clinic. For me it's been a clue that leads nowhere; for you, sir, who knows?"

He looked at Skoda searchingly.

"Yes, well . . . Are you still working in the mornings? Dissecting?"

Ignaz Philipp nodded. He looked down.

"That poor Kolletschka, a great loss, to you, particularly. . . ."

"I'll never forget him. Nor you, sir."

"And to go—that way. Well, we all have to go—some way. There's no remedy, you know. Still—cadaveric poisoning!"

"I don't know much about it."

"No. No one does."

"Only what happens."

"Only what happens."

He left Skoda.

He walked now to the graveyard where Kolletschka lay. It was in his mind to say good-by. Walking, he passed the morgue. He paused. He had never seen the death report. This, too, was Kolletschka, of his friend the last sentence.

He turned abruptly and went into the morgue. He entered the department of records.

He opened the file. He turned the pages. He came to the case of Jakob Kolletschka. In the kingdom of God there was the sound of blowing bugles.

He stared at the page, somberly.

He began to read.

The body of Jakob Kolletschka had died of cadaveric poisoning.

He read on. The record was plain.

It said:

In the upper extremity the lymphatic system was badly inflamed.

The veins were inflamed and swollen.

The tissues of his lungs were inflamed.

The heart was inflamed.

The inmost lining of his abdomen was inflamed, and the lining of his brain.

And wherever the murder traveled, in the abdomen, the lungs, the veins, the lymph system, the brain, the eye, there was a milky fluid. There was the odor of putrefaction. There was the clear and stinking liquor of death.

The poison had leaped through him, from his fingertip to his left eye. There were swellings there.

The lymphatic system inflamed. . . .

The veins inflamed and swollen. . . .

The record leaped out at him.

Lymphangitis . . . phlebitis . . . bilateral pleurisy . . . pericarditis . . . peritonitis . . . meningitis . . . and metastases. . . .

He heard a roaring.

He stared at the report.

He looked up. His breathing stopped. His ears rang with a clamor of Jericho. His eyes were blind with a great light.

He closed the book of records. He left the morgue. He began to walk. His mind read and reread the records. He saw the very texture of the paper. He saw the handwriting. He saw every word. And now carefully, delicately, his mind sifted the last case of puerperal fever he had dissected. He watched his knife cutting. He saw the tissues. He reported the findings. He compared them with the record he had just seen. Step by step, fact by fact, the cases tallied. There was one difference. Jakob Kolletschka had no uterus. In the woman the uterus and the cervix had been inflamed and the tubes and the ovaries. But the woman died and Kolletschka died. And the same thing had killed them both. His mind began slowly and carefully to select case after case, dead woman after dead woman. The dead were an endless procession. The cause of death was always the same. The symptoms were identical. The thing that killed Kolletschka killed the women.

Kolletschka had died following a wound.

But it was not the wound that had killed Kolletschka.

The wound was only a pinprick.

No man could die of such a tiny wound, a wound that shed perhaps four drops of blood.

What, then, killed Kolletschka?

His mind went back to the dissection.

He pictured the scalpel. He saw it enter the flesh of the cadaver. It was shiny and clean. He saw the knife after the dissection had gone on a little time. It was foul-looking, corroded, stained, tarnished. He saw the blade, black, coated with cadaveric material.

It was the cadaveric material.

There was no other answer.

The next thought was inexorable.

He saw himself dissecting women. They were dead of puerperal fever. He felt his fingers wet with the pus and the fluids of putrefaction. He saw those hands, partly wiped, entering the bodies of living women. The contagion passed from his fingers to the living tissues, to wounded tissues. He saw the women fever. He heard them scream. He saw them die.

He shook violently. He was remembering. Spurred by pity, he had plunged into dissection after dissection. He had dissected early in the mornings with Kolletschka. During the day he had dissected with the students. The more dissecting he did, the more infection he carried to the patients. And every student who dissected carried infection to the patients.

A new light blinded him. Now also the riddle of the clinics was solved. The First Clinic had a higher death rate than the Second Clinic because in the Second Clinic there were only midwives. And midwives did not do dissections.

Ignaz Philipp Semmelweis had discovered the cause of puerperal fever. . . .

He thought of the hospital. Instantly the discovery washed over him . . . a fever plucked at him to go to the wards, to apply his discovery, to begin immediately the end of the murder. It was absurdly simple. The remedy called for no special equipment. The remedy meant only the slightest change in the routine.

To end puerperal fever one simply washed one's hands.

A basin must be placed in every ward.

A pitcher of warm water.

A bar of soap.

A supply of towels.

A gray horror swept him. He trembled, thinking of the women he had killed. No more must die. There was no time to lose.

He was at the hospital before dawn. He smiled genially. He talked pleasantly to amazed attendants. He walked, exulting, from ward to ward. He walked, shuddering, past the autopsy room. Henceforth he would do no more dissecting.

He chafed to begin. He bit his lips to keep from crying out. He wanted to run through the wards, to rouse the patients, to cry to them all: "It's over, mothers! It's all over! There will be no more puerperal fever!" He mastered himself. The students arrived.

He tried to find words to begin. His eyes filled. They waited, wondering.

"There will be no more puerperal fever," he blurted suddenly. They looked at him in silence. He began again.

"I have found the secret to puerperal fever. Gentlemen—it is all over. Professor Kolletschka—as you know, he died of cadaveric poisoning. The symptoms of which he died and the symptoms of women who die of puerperal fever are identical. There is no difference. I have seen the record. They are exactly the same."

They waited. He plunged on.

"It is we who are the killers. It is the cadaveric particles clinging to our hands which pass into the bodies of the women we examine."

They gaped, waiting.

"Gentlemen," he said, his voice breaking with strain and joy, "from this day on we will all wash our hands!"

The students slumped, disappointed. They began to look at one another significantly. They looked back at him coldly.

"Is it understood? From this time forth no student—no midwife —no one in this division ever again will examine any patient without first washing his hands as he enters the ward."

There was an embarrassed silence.

"May—may one know why, sir doctor?"

He controlled the swift flash of anger. He smiled. They were students, after all. "It's simple, boys. We must wash off those cadaveric particles. That is all. That is absolutely all. Now come. Now let us wash. With us begins the end of puerperal fever."

Some laughed. Some murmured angrily. Some shrugged. They went to the basins. Obediently they washed their hands. When they had finished he was waiting for them.

"Now let me see them."

This was incredible. There was something of a nightmare about this. Slowly, reluctantly, incredulously, they held out their hands. He examined them cheerfully and thoroughly.

"Now come. Let us begin."

He walked to the wards. They followed after him. Rounds began. The tour ended. The students prepared to go to class. One of them stopped.

"I beg your pardon, sir."

"Yes? You want to know more about the discovery, eh? Naturally! Fine! Come to me any time!"

The student stared at him.

"Will it be necessary to submit to that somewhat unusual performance every morning, sir doctor?" he asked, his lips tight.

"Of course. One must be very careful now. Every morning, gentlemen. And every afternoon. In short, every time you examine the patients. You see there's nothing to it. We simply—wash."

The students lingered. They looked at one another uneasily. Another spoke.

"With respect, sir doctor. Do you not consider this a somewhat humiliating performance?"

Ignaz Philipp stopped smiling. He frowned a moment, thinking. He decided he had not understood.

"Humiliating? To wash your hands?" He smiled. "I'm afraid —my thoughts were wandering—perhaps I didn't understand. You found something objectionable?"

"Some of us are undergraduates, sir doctor. Many of us are already doctors. Will you be pleased to consider—"

"We aren't schoolboys!" a student cried out.

"As you know, sir, the midwives line up every morning in the Second Division to have their fingernails inspected. We aren't midwives, sir, we are students and doctors. It is, to say the least, undignified—"

Ignaz Philipp looked at them open-mouthed.

"But—but I have only asked you to wash your hands—"

"Your hypothesis, sir, with all respect, is still unproven—"

"Are we required to make ourselves ridiculous for the sake of an incredible experiment?"

A vein in his left temple began to swell. It pulsed visibly.

"Enough!" he shouted. His voice rang through the wards. He glared at them, still incredulous. "It is I who am ashamed. I have spoken to you as equals. I speak to you now as your superior. This division is my direct responsibility. I am from this day on, knowing what I know, responsible for every death that occurs in it. I have made my position perfectly plain. I believe puerperal fever can be eliminated by washing the hands. I tell you this. I ask you merely to wash your hands. You will wash your hands. You will do exactly as I say. If you find my requirements unsuitable, you may pursue your studies elsewhere. You may transfer to Berlin, if you like, where one out of three die. Or to Kiel, where one of four die. Or to Jena, where *all* die. You may go where you like. But here—so long as you attend this clinic—until this thing is proven otherwise—you will wash your hands!"

In medicine the age of antisepsis had begun.

Klein came on the second day. As always, rounds began at Bed 1, in the labor room. Ignaz Philipp appeared in the doorway. Klein walked toward the bed. Ignaz Philipp walked quickly to bar his way. With a nod he tactfully indicated the basin. Klein looked.

"What's that for?"

"To wash your hands, sir director," Ignaz Philipp said in a low voice.

Klein drew back. His face reddened.

"Have you lost your senses? Is this some joke, Doctor?"

"I have made a discovery, sir director, which I believe will end puerperal fever. I am positive I have discovered the cause. The remedy is simply washing the hands. It's really not much to ask, is it, sir director?"

Klein looked uncertainly at his hands.

"Why was I not informed? If there is to be any change in the routine of this division I am instantly to be informed. You are aware of that, Doctor?"

"You were not available, sir director. But I am happy to explain —to tell you all the circumstances—"

"If you have discoveries, Dr. Semmelweis, there is a certain, definite, well-known order for their presentation. One makes a report. One presents the report to one's director. One receives the director's permission to proceed."

"I put the report on your desk this morning, sir. I entered the procedure yesterday in the journal."

"But you began before you received permission. I am responsible for this division. I must remind you, you are only first assistant. If you execute unsanctioned ideas, and the patients die, it is I who am responsible. And is it possible, Dr. Semmelweis, that you have forgotten the code of ethics? Is it possible that you are now prepared to experiment on patients?"

Resolutely, his eyes dim with rage, his pulse pounding, Ignaz

Philipp kept his voice even. Klein was no student. He was Klein. His dignity was offended. When he understood—

"The patients were hardly in peril, sir. The students and the midwives merely washed their hands."

"Morning rounds is not the time to begin some innovation based on a flight of your imagination. Order must be and will be preserved, Dr. Semmelweis. From now on—"

"Not imagination, sir director. Not imagination, but proof! If you have read the report I submitted, you will recall that I examined the death report of Dr. Kolletschka. I found that his tissues showed the same changes as the tissues of women dead of puerperal fever. That the dissecting knife carried into his body cadaveric particles which—"

"I am familiar with your report. It is not necessary to quote it to me. I am familiar with every comma in it. I pride myself, Dr. Semmelweis, on detail. I suggest you do likewise. I have read the full details of the coincidence. And now, if you please, stand out of my way—"

Ignaz Philipp reddened with rage. He barred Klein's way. His hands clenched.

"Will you accept the responsibility, then, of examining these women with unwashed hands? For I must tell you I intend to report this discovery."

"You have told me nothing of proven medical value."

"I am not fighting for myself now, Dr. Klein. I am fighting for these women. I have shown you plainly a means by which it is, to say the least, extremely probable that we can reduce the death rate in the First Division. I suggest to you, now, that such a reduction will be to your credit. I have found a means of ending puerperal fever. It is not expensive. It does not demand great change in routine. It cannot affect the patients adversely. It is simply washing the hands."

Klein had grown a little pale. He stared at Ignaz Philipp fixedly. Ignaz Philipp waited. Klein licked his thin lips.

"This is most irregular, Dr. Semmelweis. However—"

He walked to the basin.

"With respect, sir director—a most careful washing."

Klein stiffened. He hesitated a moment. Then he began to wash harder.

At the end of May the death rate in the First Division had dropped from 18.26 per cent to 12.24 per cent.

He was beside himself with joy. But soon he frowned.

It was not enough.

Soap and water cleansed the hands. But wash as they would those students who dissected longest still wore on their hands the odor of the death room. The most conscientious students could kill the most patients.

What shall I use? he asked himself. What shall I use against these deadly particles?

Again his memory took him back to chemistry class. Again he heard the professor . . .

"I deduced instantly you had just come from an anatomy lecture. A peculiar odor accompanied you. The odor was chlorine gas—*and chlorine is a most effective agent in destroying contagion and putrid exhalations of all kinds* . . ."

Liquor Chlorina . . . *!* He smiled grimly.

That day he ordered a quantity. He made a solution.

"Soap and water," he told the students at evening rounds, "is only partly effective. The odor of decay lingers. That is because the smallest particles are clinging to your hands in tiny crevices. From now on we will wash our hands in this solution."

There were angry murmurs. They turned sullen or exasperated faces upon him.

"Wash," he said. "Wash or leave the class."

They washed. He made the attendants wash in the strong-smelling solution. He made the midwives wash in it. They gritted their teeth. They daggered him with looks of hatred. They washed.

In this time Ignaz Philipp walked the earth in tumult. Night and day became the same to him. He seldom went to bed. Often he slept sitting up, in the labor ward. His vigil was almost unceasing. He watched any person who approached a patient. He looked at the journal twenty times a day. Elation kept his heart pounding. Every hour and every moment was filled with the thunder of discovery.

June ended.

The records were summed.

The death rate had dropped from 12.24 per cent to 2.38 per cent.

The wards were quieter now. The screaming had died down. The faces of the women did not implore so much. Here and there in their beds there was even a timid smile. Furtively, hope had begun.

Toward the middle of June, Klein summoned him.

"I find that your experiments have become quite costly. Your use of Liquor Chlorina is costing us at least fifty kreutzer per patient. You will discontinue using it immediately."

Ignaz Philipp wandered to the wards dazed. He called the head midwife. He placed her in charge. He went to Skoda. He asked for the use of his library. He scanned rapidly through chemistry textbooks. He found the works of the great Justus von Leibig. He read them for hours. He made a great pile of notes. He left Skoda. He went to a pharmacy. He bought chemicals.

When he returned to the Lying-in Division it was night. He went directly to the autopsy room. He mixed a solution. He removed the sheet from a cadaver. It had been prepared for demonstration of deliveries. He plunged his hands into the cavity. He rubbed them together. He poured over his hands the solution he had prepared. Then he smelled his fingers. The odor of putrefaction was still strong.

He made another solution. He repeated the experiment. He discarded the solution. He made another. . . .

At about three o'clock in the morning he mixed a solution of water and chlorinated lime. He plunged his hands into the corpse. He used the solution. The odor had disappeared.

He set down the proportions of the solution. He estimated the cost. The total came to less than a kreutzer per patient. He smiled grimly.

The next morning Liquor Chlorina had been removed from beside the washbasins. In its stead was a large bottle of chlorinated-lime solution. On Klein's desk lay a full report, together with costs.

The work went on.

July ended.

The records were summed.

The death rate had sunk from 2.38 per cent to 1.20 per cent.

The news swept the hospital and the university.

Skoda, Hebra, and Rokitansky now began to spread Ignaz Philipp's doctrine. Haller attempted to compliment Klein.

"I hope, my dear Primarius," Klein said contemptuously, "that you are not of that number who regard this coincidence with the respect due a scientific fact. Rest assured, sir, welcome as your compliments are, your confidence in that young man is misplaced. His results are coincidence, sir. Pure coincidence."

"They appear to be facts, Doctor."

"Oh yes," said Klein. He smiled.

In August the death rate rose a little. It had been 1.20 per cent. Now it was 1.89 per cent.

Suddenly the death rate leaped to 5.25 per cent.

On a day in September Ignaz Philipp entered a ward in time

to see four students pass by the basin, stop at a bed, prepare to thrust their unwashed hands into the body of a woman who had just delivered a child.

For an instant he could not move. He was stupefied.

A student pulled back the coverlet.

"Now, Mother—"

The student bent over.

Ignaz Philipp rushed from the end of the ward.

"Gentlemen!" he shouted.

The students whirled.

"You stupid imbeciles! You clod-brained—you irresponsible—are you gone mad? Are you killers?"

They shrank, mortified, their faces burning, the patients listening.

"I don't like being talked to that way," one cried.

"Would you rather I took the sole of my shoe to you? Do you know what you're doing? Do you know what my orders are?"

"Look here, Doctor, with all respect, there are patients here—"

"No thanks to you!"

"Really, Doctor, these patients have gotten well before without any of this childish handwashing in your foul-smelling solutions—"

"You will leave the class. You will report to Professor Haller. You will not return to class. I will not have you."

The others fell silent instantly.

"I am not going to Professor Haller. I am going to another university. Some place where they behave with propriety and respect."

"You will leave instantly. Where you go is a matter of indifference to me. You will not now or ever return to this class. You are dismissed for insubordination and disobedience. That report will follow you wherever you go. And if you take my advice, you will leave medicine. You will cure more patients, resigned, than ever you will as a doctor. Now go."

The student left the ward in silence, passing red-faced between the rows of watching patients.

He paused in the doorway.

"You don't think that's the first time any of us have examined without washing our hands, do you?" he called mockingly. Then he disappeared down the corridor.

Ignaz Philipp turned slowly to the remaining students.

"Is this true?"

"Well, sir doctor, the fact is—"

"Is what he says true?"

They hung their heads.

"I have explained to you—I have told you why cleanliness is necessary—you have seen the results with your own eyes—and you *still* don't wash your hands? You deliberately flout me? You sneak? You evade for the joy of rebellion? You take these women's lives in your hands—for a whim?"

He spoke in a low voice. He could not believe it. His eyes were full of horror.

"How long has this been going on? How often—"

"Not many times, sir doctor."

"Just once or twice—"

"Just to see what would happen—"

"Come," said Ignaz Philipp tiredly. "Come. I will show you what will happen."

He took them into the labor room. In a far bed, behind a screen, a woman was dying of puerperal fever. A great stench rose from about the bed. They stood by the bedside. She no longer saw them. Her eyes were glazed. Her breath left her chest painfully and returned in slow agony.

"Let us sit here, gentlemen. Let us sit here to the last. Let us watch her die."

And so they sat until the woman breathed her last. . . .

In October, in the First Division, there were two hundred and seventy-eight deliveries. The mortality was 3.95 per cent.

"Now," said Skoda, "I'm willing to think that perhaps we have found something."

"Wait," said Ignaz Philipp. "You have seen nothing."

In the first week of November, in the First Division, there were no deaths from puerperal fever.

"There's no longer any use in waiting," said Skoda.

"What shall we do?" Rokitansky asked.

"You, Hebra, you and I shall see Klein. He is the one to announce it."

"Then tomorrow, my boy, be on your good behavior," said Rokitansky.

In the afternoon Ignaz Philipp watched from a ward as Skoda and Hebra walked toward Klein's office.

He did not see them leave.

In the evening he went quickly to Rokitansky's house. Skoda was there, and Hebra.

"We started with you," said Hebra to Ignaz Philipp. "We reviewed your work as a student, your postgraduate work, your long hours, the amount of work you did without complaint— we went over everything. We told him, God forgive us, how you respected him."

"The best we got from that," said Skoda, "was the response that you were a radical, a troublemaker, a man without order or tact or respect for duly-constituted authority.

"We proceeded to the discovery. We showed him that it had become general knowledge throughout the hospital and university that you had hit upon something that might well be a boon to humanity. We begged him to face the records, to acknowledge the falling death rate, to join in the plan to eliminate puerperal fever.

"It was then," said Skoda, "I offered him full credit for the discovery."

He paused.

"He was shocked," said Skoda. "He was shocked to his very core."

"He looked frightened," said Hebra.

"He considers the whole thing a wild concept, an irresponsible experiment which sooner or later will bring ridicule and contempt upon the whole Lying-in Division."

"He thought we were trying to trap him into being chief target for what he's sure will follow."

"Did you show him the figures?" demanded Ignaz Philipp.

"He said: 'Anything can be done with figures, gentlemen. We are all familiar enough with coincidence.' I asked him point-blank: 'Do you consider these figures a coincidence, Professor?' And he looked at me and blinked and said: 'Do you, sir professor, consider them anything else?'"

The mortality rate dropped steadily. Day followed day and there were no deaths. December ended. The mortality rate for the First Division was 2.93 per cent. Eight had died out of two hundred and seventy-three.

"Well, Hebra?" said Skoda.

Hebra, editor of the *Vienna Medical Society Journal*, smiled.

"I had it written four days ago. And you?"

"I'm going to write to Prague. To Nadherny himself."

"And I," said Rokitansky, "shall put on my top hat and my ribbons and make a formal visit to Haller."

They turned to Ignaz Philipp.

"What are you going to do?"

He stood smiling at them, his eyes full of tears.

"I am going home and thank God for such friends. With Klein —one doesn't expect much. With the students—well, even so not all of them are indifferent. But when the great men of the medical world—when Nadherny—when the others read the great *Vienna Medical Journal*—now, now I am happy. Now I know it is all over.

In a month the murder will stop. My friends . . . my very dear friends. . . ."

Skoda wrote that night to Von Nadherny, head of the University of Prague.

In the *Vienna Medical Society Journal*, one of the most widely read medical periodicals in the world, Ferdinand Hebra, editor and head of Vienna University's Department of Skin Diseases, wrote for the world to see:

EXPERIENCE OF THE HIGHEST IMPORTANCE
CONCERNING THE ETIOLOGY
OF EPIDEMIC PUERPERAL FEVER
AT THE LYING-IN HOSPITAL

The Editor of this Journal feels it is his duty to communicate to the medical profession . . . the following observations made by Dr. Semmelweis, Assistant in the First Obstetric Clinic in the General Hospital of this city. . . .

Dr. Semmelweis . . . for five years at the hospital . . . thoroughly instructed . . . for the last two years has devoted special attention to the subject of midwifery and has undertaken the task of inquiring into the causes . . . of the prevailing epidemic puerperal processes. . . .

. . . observations aroused in him the thought that in lying-in hospitals . . . the patients might be inoculated by the accoucheur himself . . . and that puerperal fever was in most cases nothing else than cadaveric infection.

In one of the world's most widely read medical journals in December, 1847, this fact was brought out clearly: Puerperal fever is in most cases a cadaveric infection, but it is sometimes an infection by means of putrid exudation or discharge from a living organism. . . .

"You'll be a great man now," said Hebra. "This university will be too small for you. You have done something more than save the living. These women will die and new women will be born and there will never be a woman born who may not owe her life to what you have discovered."

"They were dying," Ignaz Philipp mumbled, embarrassed. "They were screaming and dying. If you had seen them, if you had heard them—you'd have found a way. You couldn't have stood it, either. As long as I live I'll hear them."

"You'll hear a sweeter music henceforth," said Skoda.

Louis Pasteur
Conquers Rabies

by René Vallery-Radot

With the work of Louis Pasteur, a Frenchman, and of Robert Koch, a German, the science of bacteriology attained its golden age. Pasteur laid the basis for our knowledge of infection, while Koch discovered the exact methods by which diseases are now studied. Pasteur's imagination was greater and more far-ranging. Koch's technique and laboratory skill have never been surpassed. The work of each complemented that of the other. In many cases, as in their study of anthrax, the cattle disease, each attacked the same problem without being fully aware of what the other was doing.

Pasteur's origins were humble. He was born the son of a tanner in 1822, and became a professor of chemistry at Lille, the center of a famous French wine-growing region. Here he proved that the souring of wine and of milk, as well as the rancidity of butter, were all caused by the wrong kinds of microbes. His method of preventing this "sickness"—the heating process known as pasteurization—is used to the present day.

Could the sicknesses of animals and humans have causes similar to those of wine and milk? This was the next great question which Pasteur examined. He began with the lowly but important silkworm. The making of silk was another of France's great industries, and the silkworms were dying of a mysterious disease. Again Pasteur proved that bacteria were responsible and showed the growers how to avoid contagion. Then he went on to a still more important discovery. He had grown the bacterium of chicken cholera in test tubes and by giving fresh cultures to healthy chickens had caused them to sicken and die. But in one of his experiments he used an old culture and discovered that while the chickens sickened, they did not die. Later, when he gave these same chickens live cholera germs, they failed to catch the disease. Something in the weakened germs had made them immune.

Pasteur was to use this technique in preparing a vaccine which protected cattle against anthrax. Then, in a series of dramatic experiments, he used it on human beings to defeat the horrible disease known as hydrophobia or rabies. His first patient was a young boy who had been bitten by a mad dog. His name was Joseph Meister, a name which has become famous in medicine. His story is told in the selection that follows.

Amid the various researches undertaken in his laboratory, one study was placed by Pasteur above every other, one mystery constantly haunted his mind—that of hydrophobia.

The two first mad dogs brought into the laboratory were given to Pasteur, in 1880, by M. Bourrel, an old army veterinary surgeon who had long been trying to find a remedy for hydrophobia. He had invented a preventive measure which consisted in filing down the teeth of dogs, so that they should not bite into the skin; in 1874 he had written that vivisection threw no light on that disease, the laws of which were "impenetrable to science until now."

One of the two dogs he sent was suffering from what is called *dumb madness:* his jaw hung, half opened and paralyzed, his tongue was covered with foam, and his eyes full of wistful anguish; the other made ferocious darts at anything held out to him, with a rabid fury in his bloodshot eyes, and, in the hallucinations of his delirium, gave vent to haunting, despairing howls.

Much confusion prevailed at that time regarding this disease, its seat, its causes, and its remedy. Three things seemed positive: first, that the rabic virus was contained in the saliva of the mad animals; second, that it was communicated through bites; and third, that the period of incubation might vary from a few days to several months. Clinical observation was reduced to complete impotence; perhaps experiments might throw some light on the subject.

One day, Pasteur having wished to collect a little saliva from the jaws of a rabid dog, so as to obtain it directly, two of Bourrel's assistants undertook to drag a mad bulldog, foaming at the mouth, from its cage; they seized it by means of a lasso, and stretched it on a table. These two men, thus associated with Pasteur in the same danger, with the same calm heroism, held the struggling, ferocious animal down with their powerful hands, while the scientist drew, by means of a glass tube held between his lips, a few drops of the deadly saliva.

But the same uncertainty followed the inoculation of the saliva; the incubation was so slow that weeks and months often elapsed while the result of an experiment was being anxiously awaited. Evidently the saliva was not a sure agent for experiments, and if more knowledge was to be obtained, some other means had to be found of obtaining it.

As the number of cases observed became larger, he felt a growing conviction that hydrophobia has its seat in the nervous system, and particularly in the medulla oblongata.*

As long as the virus has not reached the nervous centers, it may sojourn for weeks or months in some point of the body; this explains the slowness of certain incubations, and the fortunate escapes after some bites from rabid dogs.

It then occurred to Pasteur to inoculate the rabic virus directly on the surface of a dog's brain. The experiment was attempted: a

* The lowest part of the brain, situated where it joins the spinal cord. —Eds.

dog under chloroform was fixed to the operating board, and a small, round portion of the cranium removed by means of a trephine (a surgical instrument somewhat similar to a fret saw); the tough fibrous membrane called the dura mater, being thus exposed, was then injected with a small quantity of the prepared virus. The wound was washed with carbolic and the skin stitched together, the whole thing lasting but a few minutes. The dog, on returning to consciousness, seemed quite the same as usual. But after fourteen days hydrophobia appeared: rabid fury, characteristic howls, the tearing up and devouring of his bed, delirious hallucination, and, finally, paralysis and death.

A method was therefore found by which rabies was contracted surely and swiftly. Trephinings were again performed on chloroformed animals—Pasteur had a great horror of useless sufferings, and always insisted on anesthesia. In every case, characteristic hydrophobia occurred after inoculation on the brain. "Since this unknown being is living," thought Pasteur, "we must cultivate it; let us try the brain of living rabbits; it would indeed be an experimental feat!"

As soon as a trephined and inoculated rabbit died paralyzed, a little of his rabic medulla was inoculated to another; each inoculation succeeded another, and the time of incubation became shorter and shorter, until, after a hundred uninterrupted inoculations, it came to be reduced to seven days.

Pasteur was not yet satisfied with the immense progress marked by infallible inoculation and the shortened incubation; he now wished to decrease the degrees of virulence. He abstracted a fragment of the medulla from a rabbit which had just died of rabies; this fragment was suspended by a thread in a sterilized phial. As the medulla gradually became dry, its virulence decreased, until, at the end of fourteen days, it had become absolutely extinguished. This now inactive medulla was crushed and mixed with pure water, and injected under the skin of some dogs. The next day they were inoculated with medulla which had been desiccating for thirteen days, and so on, using increased virulence until the medulla was used of a rabbit dead the same day. These dogs might now be bitten by rabid dogs given them as companions for a few minutes, or submitted to the intracranial inoculations of the deadly virus: they resisted both.

The subject of hydrophobia goes back to the remotest antiquity; one of Homer's warriors calls Hector a mad dog. The supposed allusions to it to be found in Hippocrates are of the vaguest, but Aristotle is quite explicit when speaking of canine rabies and of its transmission from one animal to the other through bites. He gives expression, however, to the singular opinion that man is not subject to it. More than three hundred years later we come to Celsus, who describes this disease, unknown or unnoticed until then. "The patient," said Celsus, "is tortured at the same time by thirst and by an invincible repulsion toward water." He counseled cauterization of the wound with a red-hot iron and also with various caustics and corrosives.

Pliny the Elder, a worthy precursor of village quacks, recommended the livers of mad dogs as a cure; it was not a successful one. Galen, who opposed this, had a no less singular recipe, a compound of crayfish eyes. Later, the shrine of St. Hubert in Belgium was credited with miraculous cures.

Sea bathing, unknown in France until the reign of Louis XIV, became a fashionable cure for hydrophobia, Dieppe sands being supposed to offer wonderful curing properties.

In 1780 a prize was offered for the best method of treating hydrophobia, and won by a pamphlet entitled *Dissertation sur la Rage*, written by a surgeon major by the name of Le Roux.

This very sensible treatise concluded by recommending cauterization, now long forgotten, instead of the various quack remedies which had so long been in vogue, and the use of butter of antimony.

Le Roux did not allude in his paper to certain tenacious and cruel prejudices, which had caused several hydrophobic persons, or persons merely suspected of hydrophobia, to be killed like wild beasts, shot, poisoned, strangled, or suffocated.

It was supposed in some places that hydrophobia could be transmitted through the mere contact of the saliva or even by the breath of the victims; people who had been bitten were in terror of what might be done to them. A girl, bitten by a mad dog and taken to the Hôtel Dieu Hospital on May 8, 1780, begged that she might not be suffocated!

Those dreadful occurrences must have been only too frequent, for in 1810 a philosopher asked the government to enact a bill in the following terms: "It is forbidden, under pain of death, to strangle, suffocate, bleed to death, or in any other way murder individuals suffering from rabies, hydrophobia, or any disease causing fits, convulsions, furious and dangerous madness; all necessary precautions against them being taken by families or public authorities."

In 1819 newspapers related the death of an unfortunate hydrophobe, smothered between two mattresses; it was said apropos of this murder that "it is the doctor's duty to repeat that this disease cannot be transmitted from man to man, and that there is therefore no danger in nursing hydrophobia patients." Though old and fantastic remedies were still in vogue in remote country places, cauterization was the most frequently employed; if the wounds were somewhat deep, it was recommended to use long, sharp, and pointed needles, and to push them well in, even if the wound was on the face.

One of Pasteur's childish recollections (it happened in October, 1831) was the impression of terror produced throughout the Jura by the advent of a rabid wolf who went biting men and beasts on his way. Pasteur had seen an Arboisian by the name of Nicole being cauterized with a red-hot iron at the smithy near his father's house. The persons who had been bitten on the hands and head succumbed to hydrophobia, some of them amid horrible sufferings; there were eight victims in the immediate neighborhood. Nicole was saved. For years the whole region remained in dread of that mad wolf.

On March 28, 1885, Pasteur wrote to his friend Jules Vercel— "I have some new experiments on rabies on hand which will take some months. I am demonstrating this year that dogs can be vaccinated, or made refractory to rabies *after* they have been bitten by mad dogs.

"I have not yet dared to treat human beings after bites from rabid dogs; but the time is not far off, and I am much inclined to begin by myself—inoculating myself with rabies, and then arresting the consequences; for I am beginning to feel very sure of my results."

It was in the year 1884 that Pasteur succeeded in vaccinating dogs so that they became immune to the disease after vaccination. Yet vaccination was not a practical way of eliminating the disease. As Pasteur's biographer points out, "there were 100,000 dogs in Paris, about 2,500,000 more in the provinces: vaccination necessitates several preventive inoculations; innumerable kennels would have to be built for the purpose, to say nothing of the expense of keeping the dogs and of providing a trained staff capable of performing the difficult and dangerous operations." The solution obviously lay in a different direction. A method must be discovered of preventing rabies from developing after a dog or a human being had been bitten.

For this purpose Pasteur conducted a series of experiments over

*a period of months which were similar to those already described.
Animals were first inoculated with rabies or exposed to the bites
of rabid dogs. Thereafter, they were treated with gradually more
virulent doses of the vaccine, and just as in the cases of animals
which had been vaccinated before exposure, they failed to contract
the disease. It was the success of these new experiments that made
Pasteur willing to risk his own life. That was not the same thing as
risking the life of another, but circumstances forced his hand.
When little Joseph Meister, bitten by a mad dog, appeared at his
laboratory, he knew the agonizing decision must be made.*

On Monday, July 6, Pasteur saw a little Alsatian boy, Joseph
Meister, enter his laboratory, accompanied by his mother. He was
only nine years old, and had been bitten two days before by a mad
dog at Meissengott, near Schlestadt.

The child, going alone to school by a little by-road, had been
attacked by a furious dog and thrown to the ground. Too small to
defend himself, he had only thought of covering his face with his
hands. A bricklayer, seeing the scene from a distance, arrived,
and succeeded in beating the dog off with an iron bar; he picked up
the boy, covered with blood and saliva. The dog went back to his
master, Théodore Vone, a grocer at Meissengott, whom he bit on
the arm. Vone seized a gun and shot the animal, whose stomach
was found to be full of hay, straw, pieces of wood, etc. When little
Meister's parents heard all these details they went, full of anxiety,
to consult Dr. Weber, at Villé, that same evening. After cauter-
izing the wounds with carbolic, Dr. Weber advised Mme. Meister
to start for Paris, where she could relate the facts to one who was
not a physician, but who would be the best judge of what could
be done in such a serious case. Théodore Vone, anxious on his own
and on the child's account, decided to come also.

Pasteur reassured him; his clothes had wiped off the dog's saliva, and his shirt sleeve was intact. He might safely go back to Alsace, and he promptly did so.

Pasteur's emotion was great at the sight of the fourteen wounds of the little boy, who suffered so much that he could hardly walk. What should he do for this child? Could he risk the preventive treatment which had been constantly successful on his dogs? Pasteur was divided between his hopes and his scruples, painful in their acuteness. Before deciding on a course of action, he made arrangements for the comfort of this poor woman and her child, alone in Paris, and gave them an appointment for five o'clock, after the Institute meeting. He did not wish to attempt anything without having seen Vulpian (a member of the official Commission that had been appointed to investigate his work). Since the Rabies Commission had been constituted, Pasteur had formed a growing esteem for the great judgment of Vulpian.

Vulpian expressed the opinion that Pasteur's experiments on dogs were sufficiently conclusive to authorize him to foresee the same success in human pathology. Why not try this treatment? added the professor, usually so reserved. Was there any other efficacious treatment against hydrophobia? If at least the cauterizations had been made with a red-hot iron! But what was the good of carbolic acid twelve hours after the accident? If the almost certain danger which threatened the boy were weighed against the chances of snatching him from death, Pasteur would see that it was more than a right, that it was a duty to apply antirabic inoculation to little Meister.

This was also the opinion of Dr. Grancher, whom Pasteur consulted. M. Grancher worked at the laboratory; he and Dr. Straus might claim to be the first two French physicians who took up the study of bacteriology.

Vulpian and M. Grancher examined little Meister in the evening, and, seeing the number of bites, some of which, on one hand especially, were very deep, they decided on performing the first inoculation immediately; the substance chosen was fourteen days old and had quite lost its virulence: it was to be followed by further inoculations gradually increasing in strength.

It was a very slight operation, a mere injection into the side of a few drops of a liquid prepared with some fragments of medulla oblongata. The child, who cried very much before the operation, soon dried his tears when he found the slight prick was all that he had to undergo.

Pasteur had had a bedroom comfortably arranged for the mother and child in the old Rollin College, and the little boy was very happy amid the various animals—chickens, rabbits, white mice, guinea pigs, etc.; he begged and easily obtained of Pasteur the life of several of the youngest of them.

"All is going well," Pasteur wrote to his son-in-law on July 11: "the child sleeps well, has a good appetite, and the inoculated matter is absorbed into the system from one day to another without leaving a trace. It is true that I have not yet come to the test inoculations, which will take place on Tuesday, Wednesday, and Thursday. If the lad keeps well during the three following weeks, I think the experiment will be safe to succeed. I shall send the child and his mother back to Meissengott (near Schlestadt) in any case on August 1, giving these good people detailed instruction as to the observations they are to record for me. I shall make no statement before the end of the vacation."

But, as the inoculations were becoming more virulent, Pasteur became a prey to anxiety. "My dear children," wrote Mme. Pasteur, "your father has had another bad night; he is dreading the last inoculations on the child. And yet there can be no drawing back now! The boy continues in perfect health."

Renewed hopes were expressed in the following letter from Pasteur—

"My dear René, I think great things are coming to pass. Joseph

Meister has just left the laboratory. The three last inoculations have left some pink marks under the skin, gradually widening and not at all tender. There is some action, which is becoming more intense as we approach the final inoculation, which will take place on Thursday, July 16. The lad is very well this morning, and has slept well, though slightly restless; he has a good appetite and no feverishness. He had a slight hysterical attack yesterday."

The letter ended with an affectionate invitation. "Perhaps one of the great medical facts of the century is going to take place; you would regret not having seen it!"

Pasteur was going through a succession of hopes, fears, anguish, and an ardent yearning to snatch little Meister from death; he could no longer work. At nights, feverish visions came to him of his child whom he had seen playing in the garden, suffocating in the mad struggles of hydrophobia, like the dying child he had seen at the Hôpital Trousseau in 1880. Vainly his experimental genius assured him that the virus of that most terrible of diseases was about to be vanquished, that humanity was about to be delivered from this dread horror—his human tenderness was stronger than all, his accustomed ready sympathy for the sufferings and anxieties of others was for the nonce centered in "the dear lad."

The treatment lasted ten days; Meister was inoculated twelve times. The virulence of the medulla used was tested by trephinings on rabbits, and proved to be gradually stronger. Pasteur even inoculated on July 16, at 11 A.M., some medulla only one day old, bound to give hydrophobia to rabbits after only seven days' incubation; it was the surest test of the immunity and preservation due to the treatment.

Cured from his wounds, delighted with all he saw, gaily running about as if he had been in his own Alsatian farm, little Meister, whose blue eyes now showed neither fear nor shyness, merrily received the last inoculation; in the evening, after claiming a kiss from "Dear Monsieur Pasteur," as he called him, he went to bed and slept peacefully. Pasteur spent a terrible night of insomnia; in those slow, dark hours of night, when all vision is distorted, Pasteur, losing sight of the accumulation of experiments which guaranteed his success, imagined that the little boy would die.

The treatment being now completed, Pasteur left little Meister to the care of Dr. Grancher (the lad was not to return to Alsace until July 27) and consented to take a few days' rest. He spent them with his daughter in a quiet, almost deserted country place in Burgundy, but without, however, finding much restfulness in the beautiful peaceful scenery; he lived in constant expectation of Dr. Grancher's daily telegram or letter containing news of Joseph Meister.

By the time he went to the Jura, Pasteur's fears had almost disappeared. He wrote from Arbois to his son August 3, 1885: "Very good news last night of the bitten lad. I am looking forward with great hopes to the time when I can draw a conclusion. It will be thirty-one days tomorrow since he was bitten."

. . . On his return to Paris, Pasteur found himself obliged to hasten the organization of a "service" for the preventive treatment of hydrophobia after a bite. The mayor of Villers-Farlay, in the Jura, wrote to him that, on October 14, a shepherd had been cruelly bitten by a rabid dog.

Six little shepherd boys were watching over their sheep in a meadow; suddenly they saw a large dog passing along the road, with hanging, foaming jaws.

"A mad dog!" they exclaimed. The dog, seeing the children, left the road and charged them; they ran away shrieking, but the eldest of them, J. B. Jupille, fourteen years of age, bravely turned back in order to protect the flight of his comrades. Armed with his whip, he confronted the infuriated animal, who flew at him and seized his left hand. Jupille, wrestling with the dog, succeeded in kneeling on him, and forcing his jaws open in order to disengage his left hand; in so doing, his right hand was seriously bitten in its turn; finally, having been able to get hold of the animal by the neck, Jupille called to his little brother to pick up his whip which had fallen during the struggle, and securely fastened the dog's jaws with the lash. He then took his wooden sabot, with which he battered the dog's head, after which, in order to be sure that it could do no further harm, he dragged the body down to a little stream in the meadow, and held the head under water for several minutes. Death being now certain, and all danger removed from his comrades, Jupille returned to Villers-Farlay.

While the boy's wounds were being bandaged, the dog's carcass was fetched, and a necropsy took place the next day. The two veterinary surgeons who examined the body had not the slightest hesitation in declaring that the dog was rabid.

The mayor of Villers-Farlay, who had been to see Pasteur during the summer, wrote to tell him that this lad would die a victim of his own courage unless the new treatment intervened. The answer came immediately: Pasteur declared that, after five years' study, he had succeeded in making dogs refractory to rabies, even six or eight days after being bitten; that he had only once yet applied his method to a human being, but that once with success, in the case of little Meister, and that, if Jupille's family consented, the boy might be sent to him. "I shall keep him near me in a room of my laboratory; he will be watched and need not go to bed; he will merely receive a daily prick, not more painful than a pin-prick."

The family, on hearing this letter, came to an immediate decision; but, between the day when he was bitten and Jupille's arrival in Paris, six whole days had elapsed, while in Meister's case there had only been two and a half!

Yet, however great were Pasteur's fears for the life of this tall lad, who seemed quite surprised when congratulated on his cou-

rageous conduct, they were not what they had been in the first
instance—he felt much greater confidence.

A few days later, on October 26, Pasteur in a statement at the
Academy of Sciences described the treatment followed for Meister.
Three months and three days had passed, and the child remained
perfectly well. Then he spoke of his new attempt. Vulpian rose.

"The Academy will not be surprised," he said, "if, as a member
of the Medical and Surgical Section, I ask to be allowed to express
the feelings of admiration inspired in me by M. Pasteur's statement.
I feel certain that those feelings will be shared by the whole of the
medical profession.

"Hydrophobia, that dread disease against which all thera-
peutic measures had hitherto failed, has at last found a remedy.
M. Pasteur, who has been preceded by no one in this path, has been
led by a series of investigations, unceasingly carried on for several
years, to create a method of treatment, by means of which the development of hydrophobia can *infallibly* be prevented in a patient
recently bitten by a rabid dog. I say infallibly, because, after what
I have seen in M. Pasteur's laboratory, I do not doubt the constant
success of this treatment when it is put into full practice a few days
only after a rabic bite." . . .

Bouley, then chairman of the Academy, rose to speak in his
turn.

"We are entitled to say that the date of the present meeting will
remain forever memorable in the history of medicine, and glorious
for French science; for it is that of one of the greatest steps ever
accomplished in the medical order of things—a progress realized
by the discovery of an efficacious means of preventive treatment
for a disease the incurable nature of which was a legacy handed
down by one century to another. From this day, humanity is
armed with a means of fighting the fatal disease of hydrophobia
and of preventing its onset. It is to M. Pasteur that we owe this,
and we could not feel too much admiration or too much gratitude

for the efforts on his part which have led to such a magnificent result. . . ."

As soon as Pasteur's paper was published, people bitten by rabid dogs began to arrive at the laboratory from all sides. The "service" of hydrophobia became the chief business of the day. Every morning Eugène Viala spent preparing the fragments of marrow used for inoculations: in a little room permanently kept at a temperature of 20° to 23° C. stood rows of sterilized flasks, their tubular openings closed by plugs of cotton wool. Each flask contained a rabic marrow, hanging from the stopper by a thread and gradually drying up by the action of some fragments of caustic potash lying at the bottom of the flask. Viala cut those marrows into small pieces by means of scissors previously put through a flame, and placed them in small sterilized glasses; he then added a few drops of veal broth and pounded the mixture with a glass rod. The vaccinal liquid was now ready; each glass was covered with a paper cover, and bore the date of the medulla used, the earliest of which was fourteen days old. For each patient under the treatment from a certain date there was a whole series of little glasses. . . . The date and circumstances of the bites and the veterinary surgeon's certificate were entered in a register, and the patients were divided into series according to the degree of virulence which was to be inoculated on each day of the period of treatment.

Pasteur took a personal interest in each of his patients, helping those who were poor and illiterate to find suitable lodgings in the great capital. Children especially inspired him with a loving solicitude. But his pity was mingled with terror, when, on November 9, a little girl of ten was brought to him who had been severely bitten on the head by a mountain dog, on October 3, thirty-seven days before! The wound was still suppurating. He said to himself, "This is a hopeless case: hydrophobia is no doubt about to appear immediately; it is much too late for the preventive treatment to have the least chance of success. Should I not, in the scientific interest of the method, refuse to treat this child? If the issue is fatal, all those who have already been treated will be frightened, and many bitten persons, discouraged from coming to the laboratory, may succumb to the disease!" These thoughts rapidly crossed Pasteur's mind. But he found himself unable to resist his compassion for the father and mother, begging him to try to save their child.

After the treatment was over, Louise Pelletier had returned to school, when fits of breathlessness appeared, soon followed by convulsive spasms; she could swallow nothing. Pasteur hastened to her side when these symptoms began, and new inoculations were attempted. On December 2 there was a respite of a few hours, moments of calm that inspired Pasteur with the vain hope that she might yet be saved. This delusion was a short-lived one. Pasteur spent the day by little Louise's bedside, in her parents' rooms in the Rue Dauphine. He could not tear himself away; she herself, full of affection for him, gasped out a desire that he should not go away, that he should stay with her! She felt for his hand between two spasms. Pasteur shared the grief of the father and mother. When all hope had to be abandoned: "I did so wish I could have saved your little one!" he said. And as he came down the staircase, he burst into tears.

He was obliged, a few days later, to preside at the reception of Joseph Bertrand at the Académie Française, his sad feelings little in harmony with the occasion. He read in a mournful and troubled voice the speech he had prepared during his peaceful and happy holidays at Arbois. Henry Houssaye, reporting on this ceremony in the *Journal des Débats*, wrote, "M. Pasteur ended his speech amid a torrent of applause; he received a veritable ovation. He seemed unaccountably moved. How can M. Pasteur, who has received every mark of admiration, every supreme honor, whose name is consecrated by universal renown, still be touched by anything save the discoveries of his powerful genius?" People did not realize that Pasteur's thoughts were far away from himself and from his brilliant discovery. He was thinking of the child he had been unable to snatch from the jaws of death; his mind was not with the living, but with the dead.

A telegram from New York having announced that four children, bitten by rabid dogs, were starting for Paris, many adversaries who had heard of Louise Pelletier's death were saying triumphantly that, if those children's parents had known of her fate, they would have spared them so long and useless a journey.

The four little Americans belonged to workmen's families and were sent to Paris by means of a public subscription opened in the columns of the New York *Herald*; they were accompanied by a doctor and by the mother of the youngest of them, a boy only five years old. After the first inoculation, this little boy, astonished at the insignificant prick, could not help saying, "Is this all we have come such a long journey for?" The children were received with enthusiasm on their return to New York, and were asked "many questions about the great man who had taken such care of them."

A letter dated from that time (January 14, 1886) shows that Pasteur yet found time for kindness in the midst of his world-famed occupations.

"My dear Jupille, I have received your letters, and I am much pleased with the news you give me of your health. Mme. Pasteur thanks you for remembering her. She, and everyone at the laboratory, join with me in wishing that you may keep well and improve as much as possible in reading, writing, and arithmetic. Your writing is already much better than it was, but you should take some pains with your spelling. Where do you go to school? Who teaches you? Do you work at home as much as you might? You know that Joseph Meister, who was first to be vaccinated, often writes to me; well, I think he is improving more quickly than you are, though he is only ten years old. So, mind you take pains, do not waste your time with other boys, and listen to the advice of your teachers, and of your father and mother. Remember me to

M. Perrot, the mayor of Villers-Farlay. Perhaps, without him, you would have become ill, and to be ill of hydrophobia means inevitable death; therefore you owe him much gratitude. Good-by. Keep well."

Pasteur's solicitude did not confine itself to his first two patients, Joseph Meister and the fearless Jupille, but was extended to all those who had come under his care; his kindness was like a living flame. The very little ones who then only saw in him a "kind gentleman" bending over them understood later in life, when recalling the sweet smile lighting up his serious face, that Science, thus understood, unites moral with intellectual grandeur.

Miraculous Accident:
Fleming, Florey, and Penicillin

by Milton Silverman

If Pasteur was the originator of the germ theory, Koch laid the basis for turning the theory into a science. He it was who showed how germs could be grown in test tubes and how they could be stained so that they could be more easily observed under the microscope. He also grew germs in "pure culture," uncontaminated by other bodies that might influence their growth and effect on animal and man. He proved, once for all, that specific germs caused specific diseases. His greatest triumph was proof that tuberculosis was caused not by "bad blood" or bad inheritance or bad environment or indeed by any kind of germ except the tubercule bacillus. The great bacteriologist Paul Ehrlich, writing of the meeting at which Koch described his researches on this bacillus, called it "the most majestic scientific event in which I have ever participated."

With Koch's techniques the bacteria for many other diseases—cholera, typhoid, bubonic plague, dysentery, diphtheria—were rapidly discovered. Next came prevention and treatment. Cleanliness and antiseptic methods accomplished much—as in the elimination of typhoid from drinking water. Another means of prevention depended on the vaccines that Pasteur had already developed for anthrax and rabies. Such methods were used to check diphtheria and tetanus. A different plan of attack was based on the discoveries that while many microbes were air-borne, others, like those which caused malaria, yellow fever, and Texas fever, were carried by mosquitoes and vermin. Kill the mosquitoes and the ticks and you kill the disease said such men as Ronald Ross and Walter Reed and Theobald Smith.

It was Paul Ehrlich, whom we have quoted above, who had still another idea. If, said Ehrlich, each disease is caused by a specific microbe, may not there be some specific substance—some "magic bullet"—that will seek out and kill that particular microbe without doing harm to its host— the man or animal in which it is lodged? He searched long and laboriously for such a bullet to assassinate the spirochete of syphilis. There is a legend that one of his assistants revolted against continuing the work after 605 experiments. Whether or not the legend is true, there is no doubt that with the next experiment Ehrlich discovered the famous "606," an arsenic compound that proved successful in treating the disease.

But except for 606 and a cure for sleeping sickness, the idea of a magic bullet proved largely unproductive. Laboratory workers struggled for years to add to the arsenal, but gradually abandoned this technique. It had all but fallen into limbo when two of the most sensational discoveries in the history of medicine were made. The first came almost as a by-product of the work of the German dye trust. The brick-red dye named Prontosil was found to contain a substance later identified as sulfanilamide, which had almost miraculous powers of curing pneumonia, blood poisoning, and puerperal fever. It was the first in a series of sulfa drugs which could be made cheaply and easily by chemical synthesis, and which had the power to wipe out certain diseases. There had never been anything like them.

But more and even better was to come—in the form of the antibiotics. These came not from the laboratory but from nature itself—existing in the air and soil. The first—penicillin—was discovered by one of those miraculous accidents that happen to scientists who are prepared to take advantage of them. Milton Silverman tells the story of its development.

I

It seemed there had always been Flemings around the Scotch city of Kilmarnock. They were merchants and farmers, they wove fine curtains and carpets on their hand looms, they raised cattle, and they sold milk and they made cheese as good as any to be found throughout Ayrshire.

Hugh Fleming's farm was near Darvel, not quite ten miles from Kilmarnock, on the banks of Irvine Water. He was a good, honest Scotsman, and he taught his children to use their eyes and their brains, to be patient and thrifty, and to fear God. On August 6, 1881, his wife presented him with a new son, who was named Alexander.

As a boy, young Alexander was considered a reasonably good student—perhaps a wee bit better than some—but nothing to set the world on fire. He was good at games, an excellent swimmer. When he was ready for a further education, he was sent to Kilmarnock Academy. When he finished at the Academy, he went to London and worked in a shipping office, and then decided he was ready to tackle medicine.

So, at the age of twenty-one, Alexander Fleming entered a competition for a scholarship at St. Mary's Hospital Medical School, won it, and became a medical student. When he graduated in 1908, he walked off with honors in physiology, pharmacology, medicine, pathology, forensic medicine, and hygiene, and the University Gold Medal.

One day soon after his graduation he heard of a vacancy in St. Mary's bacteriology department under Sir Almroth Wright, and he applied for the job and got it.

In those days the faculty of St. Mary's was not altogether distinguished; it was, in fact, rather second-rate, but Wright was one of the exceptions. For more than a decade he had been working on the microbes that infect the intestinal tract of man and animals, he had led the war against typhoid fever, and now he had succeeded in introducing a vaccine to prevent typhoid.

Under Wright's tutelage, Fleming began to learn about bacteria—about the ways in which they invade and attack the human body, about the body's defense system, about white blood cells, about antiseptics and serums and vaccines. He set up simple experiments, none of them very important, and he helped teach the medical students.

When World War I broke out, he went into the army medical corps with a captain's commission and was sent to Boulogne to work in the British Expeditionary Force's 13th General Hospital.

Carrying out instructions, Fleming began to look for "an improved wound antiseptic." How do you find such a thing? Well, you get bottles and vials and packets of all sorts of chemicals, and see what they do to germs. For months Fleming did exactly this. So did many of his fellow scientists. And none of them found anything that looked like a superior antiseptic. Fleming did one other thing—just for curiosity, he tested some of the standard antiseptics and some of the proposed new ones on living human cells, on the white blood corpuscles that act as the body's defense system.

"Isn't it odd," he remarked, "that some of these chemicals are better at destroying white blood cells than at killing germs? I shouldn't think they would be very practical."

Unfortunately, it was only too true that many of the harsh antiseptics already in use were almost as deadly to the patient as to the invading germs. But Fleming didn't see what he could do about it. He served out the war in his army laboratory, and then came back to St. Mary's in London. For several years he kept on with his work. All along he kept on the watch for a nontoxic germ killer—a lifesaving substance which would destroy microbes without harming healthy human tissues.

In 1922 he thought he had one. It was a substance which he called lysozyme—a microbe-dissolving chemical which he could detect in human tears, in saliva, and even in egg whites. But lysozyme was not very useful, for the microbes it could destroy were not the microbes that cause disease.

Fleming kept on with his researches. Two years later, in 1924, he worked out a novel method to measure the probable usefulness of any antiseptic. First, he said, you should measure the effect of the antiseptic on microbes and see how much it takes to kill them; second, measure the effect on white blood corpuscles, the body's own germ digesters. If the antiseptic is more toxic to white blood corpuscles than to germs, then it probably won't be very useful, but if it can kill germs without killing white blood cells, then it might be an antiseptic with real medical value.

Four more years went by and a publisher wrote to him: "We want to bring out a new book on bacteriology. Will you write the chapter on the staphylococci?"

Fleming was now the director of St. Mary's inoculation department and had become an admitted expert on the pus-forming staphylococci, the deadly little germs that grow in grapelike clusters and cause such annoying things as boils and carbuncles —and also deadly infections of the spine, the heart, and the blood.

It was an ordinary request, this note from the publisher, but it was the first in a series of accidents and coincidences that were unparalleled in the history of drugs.

Fleming replied that he would be glad to write the chapter, and set about getting his ideas and his notes into shape. There was one little experiment he wanted to try, too, before he did his writing; he'd just read a report which said that, under certain circumstances, colonies of these staphylococci could change their appearance.

So one day in the summer of 1928 the little, blue-eyed Scotch scientist began filling sterilized glass plates with sterilized jelly, covering them with sterilized glass tops, and then—when everything was ready—lifting off the covers, planting a few staphylococci, and whipping the covers back. This was the time-honored procedure to prevent contamination, to keep unwanted microbes out of the picture, and it was especially necessary in Fleming's little laboratory, for his workroom was not like the gleaming, polished, ultra-ultra-sterile laboratories of the big institutes; it was dark and it was crowded and it was not—as Fleming himself often complained—quite clean.

Weeks went by, and more and more plates of staphylococci were piled on the long table next to the window. It was September, hot and sticky, and the window was open. . . .

Fleming reached for one of the dishes of staphylococci.

He quickly lifted off the cover glass, slid the plate under his clumsy dissecting microscope, looked for a few seconds, and then put back the cover. How long had the cover been off? Two seconds? Five seconds? Ten? Whatever it was, it had been long enough.

A few days passed, and once again Fleming came upon the plate. At first glance it seemed to be all right. And then . . .

Inside the plate, over to one side, a speck of mold was growing—growing right on top of a colony of staphylococci. It was white and fluffy, somewhat like bread mold, with a touch of dark green in the center.

In hundreds, perhaps thousands of laboratories, just such an accident has happened—a cover removed for only a second too long, a spore wafted in by a breeze, and, in a few days, a contaminating growth of mold. And in all those laboratories the next step had inevitably been the same—"You use the appropriate language and chuck the contaminated plate into the sink."

He was ready to toss out this plate—and millions of human lives waited in the balance. But he stopped.

He looked and saw a miracle. It didn't look like a miracle, of course; what he saw was a colony of mold growing on top of what had been a big colony of deadly staphylococci. Away from the mold, the staphylococci were still growing luxuriantly in moist, buttery little mounds. But around the mold there was a clear zone—*a zone in which the staphylococci were obviously being dissolved!*

Another scientist might have wondered about this for a moment, and then proceeded to discard the contaminated plate and forget about it. Fleming, however, was not another scientist; he decided to look into this mold. Picking up a platinum wire, he sterilized it in a burner flame, let it cool, deftly touched it to the mold, and transplanted a bit of this to a fresh tube of microbe food. Then, for weeks, he grew and studied it; he transplanted it again and again, sometimes to other tubes and sometimes to bottles of broth.

"In broth," he wrote, "it grows on the surface as a white, fluffy growth; in a few days this becomes a dark-green, felted mass. In a few weeks the broth becomes bright yellow."

This yellow color, whatever it was—could that be the stuff that dissolved the staphylococci? Soon Fleming found that the yellow matter had nothing to do with germ killing.

Mixed with the yellow stuff was something else, a second substance which was also secreted by the mold and which also soaked all through the broth. Fleming poured off some of this broth, mixed it with colonies of staphylococci, and found that it stopped their growth. He tried it on streptococci—and it stopped them, too. It destroyed the microbes of pneumonia, diphtheria, meningitis, and gonorrhea. Against other germs—the microbes of cholera, dysentery, and typhoid—this "mold juice," as Fleming called it, was useless. It was not a complete germ killer. When it did work, however, its power was astounding; even when the mold juice was diluted as much as eight hundred times, it could still destroy microbes. This juice, he calculated, was three times stronger than carbolic acid!

And then the thought, "Anything that strong will be murder to animals or human beings. It will wreck their tissues!"

He tried it. He put the mold juice through his test with white blood cells, and found that the white blood cells were unharmed. He injected more than half an ounce of the undiluted juice into a rabbit. The rabbit scarcely batted an eye.

Now Fleming realized what he had—a new, mysterious chemical which was sheer murder to microbes but *virtually harmless to healthy tissues*.

The next step was to try it on human beings. He took some of the mold juice into the hospital wards, poured it into the raw, infected, sensitive wound of one patient, and into the eye of another. "There was no irritant effect," he reported.

But did it cure the infected wound or the sore eye? No, it did not—for the simple but unfortunate reason that Fleming and his colleague Mr. Ridley couldn't prepare enough of it to cure anything. Weeks were required for the mold to secrete enough of this stuff for even a small laboratory test. Furthermore, it was exceedingly unstable and lost its activity on the slightest excuse. Ridley tried to concentrate the material, and evaporated great quantities of the juice to a sticky mass, but he couldn't isolate the active chemical in pure form.

All they could do with it, apparently, was to name it. After Fleming had identified the mold as a member of the *Penicillium* family, the potent but still elusive microbe killer was called *penicillin*.

In May, 1929, after eight months of work, he wrote his first formal report—a simple, ten-page announcement which was eventually published in the *British Journal of Experimental Pathology*. As one of his conclusions, he wrote: "It is suggested that it may be an efficient antiseptic for application to, or injection into, areas infected with penicillin-sensitive microbes."

In the next year or two he managed to accumulate enough crude penicillin to try on a few infected wounds, chiefly carbuncles and infected sinuses. "Although the results were considered favorable," he said, "there was no miraculous success."

The publication of Fleming's paper made no great noise in the scientific world. Since the time of Pasteur, bacteriologists had suspected that various molds, fungi, bacteria, bacilli, and cocci produce substances which could destroy other microbes. Some of these substances—pyocyanase, penicillic acid (no relation to penicillin), and actinomycetin—had actually been isolated and tested, but either they destroyed the wrong kind of germ or they were too toxic to human beings.

A few men wrote to Fleming for samples of his strain of mold, and they checked parts of his work. At the London School of Hygiene, a group of chemists headed by Harold Raistrick tried their hand at improving the extraction of penicillin, but they didn't get very far.

"Raistrick succeeded only up to a point," Fleming commented later. "The bacteriologists in his institution didn't seem to think much of his research, so they didn't cooperate. He was stuck for want of bacteriologists and we were stuck for want of chemists.

"When we saw that this good chemist had failed to extract penicillin," added Fleming, "we stopped doing anything about it. If he couldn't, we couldn't."

It was 1932 when Raistrick admitted that "he couldn't." On Christmas Day of that same year Mietzsch and Klarer of the I. G. Farbenindustrie applied for a patent on a new chemical which they called prontosil. It was the first of the sulfa drugs.

The sulfa drugs could also kill microbes. They were not

altogether safe. They could not touch some of the microbes that penicillin could hit. But you could produce the sulfa drugs practically in any chemical laboratory—by the ounce, by the pound, by the ton.

Penicillin was a dead pigeon.

II

Howard Florey was born in Adelaide, Australia, in 1898, the son of a prominent boot manufacturer. He went to Kyre College and St. Peters Collegiate School, where he won a dozen prizes in chemistry, physics, mathematics, and history, and half-a-dozen scholarships. In 1917 he entered the medical school at the University of Adelaide, where he proceeded to be top man in his class for three out of four years.

In 1921 he sailed for England as a Rhodes scholar.

He stayed at Oxford for three years, listening to lectures on physiology and pathology, studying the circulation of capillaries, the nature of inflammation, learning what happens to tissues when they get sick. Then he worked for a while at Cambridge, took time out to accompany a scientific expedition to Spitzbergen, came to America in 1925 as a Rockefeller fellow, and the next year returned to work at the London Hospital.

In 1931 Florey became a big frog in a rather small puddle—professor of pathology at the University of Sheffield.

During the next few years strange things went on across the Channel in Germany. Adolf Hitler, the fanatic little house painter, organized his brown-shirted bullies. Early in 1933 Hitler was named chancellor, and laws were soon drafted to "reduce the percentage" of Jews in government, in industry, in law, in medicine, and in science. By summer thousands of Jews and other political refugees were leaving Germany to find a foreign haven.

Among those who got out was twenty-seven-year-old Ernst Boris Chain, part Russian, part German, one of the most promising young chemists in the Reich. Chain had been born in Berlin, studied chemistry and physiology at the university there, and then gone to work in the department of pathology at Berlin's great Charité Hospital. He worked on enzymes and complicated organic chemicals, on yeasts and bacteria and tissue cultures. His superiors predicted a brilliant future for him, but he saw clearly what was coming in Germany.

He left Germany and went to Cambridge University in England, where the old vitamin hunter, Sir Frederick Gowland Hopkins, gave him a place in his laboratory. Two years later, in 1935, Howard Florey—who had just been named professor of pathology at Oxford—came to Cambridge looking for a chemist. On Hopkins' recommendation, he took Chain.

Florey and Chain became friends and coworkers. They discussed each other's laboratory investigations. They answered each other's questions, Florey drawing on his excellent knowledge of tissues and disease, Chain providing new tricks in chemistry. They talked about the new wonder drugs, sulfanilamide and its cousins, which were so amazing, so miraculous, so completely practical. But the sulfas couldn't cure tuberculosis or syphilis or many other diseases. Sometimes the sulfas cured a patient of a simple streptococcus or pneumonia infection only to damage his kidneys. And sometimes there appeared a strain of streptococci or staphylococci which was untouched by the sulfas.

The sulfa drugs, they agreed, represented a tremendous advance. But they also agreed that medicine needed something better.

The something came from Fleming's work, not on penicillin but on lysozyme. Florey and Chain had been following that old scientific will-o'-the-wisp, and one day came to the decision that they should look into other antibacterial substances, perhaps some produced by microbes and fungi and other microorganisms. Chain and his young American assistant, Leslie Falk, began reading the old reports on actinomycetin and pyocyanase and bacteriophage. Finally they came upon the first report on penicillin which Alexander Fleming had written back in 1929.

Chain began growing Fleming's mold, repeating the first simple experiments in test tubes. The research was constantly interrupted by work on other laboratory projects, but nobody minded—after all, this was not a very vital job. It became vital suddenly one September morning in 1939 when a BBC broadcaster announced: "Hitler has invaded Poland." World War II was on.

Britain at war needed guns and planes and tanks. She also needed drugs—anesthetics and vaccines and especially microbe killers to fight the plagues and wound infections which always accompany war.

What about penicillin? It was still an untried, untested, unisolated agent. Now, when there were scores of essential jobs for every trained scientist, did it justify a further investment of their time? Howard Florey thought it did. He not merely gave Chain his backing, but he assigned to the job one of his best assistants, Norman Heatley, almost unbelievably patient and skillful. Arthur Duncan Gardner, Oxford's professor of bacteriology, agreed to join the expanding penicillin team. Soon there came more chemists, biochemists, bacteriologists, and pathologists. More and more big earthenware jars were delivered to the laboratory and filled with more and more gallons of mold food. Shelves were packed with containers of ethers, alcohols, ketones, esters, and every other conceivable solvent that might be used to extract penicillin.

They found that penicillin is an acid, and that it is destroyed by contact with other acids. They found that penicillin can be extracted with ether or chloroform or amyl acetate, with its odor of freshly crushed pears. And, of tremendous importance, Chain reported that there is a way to store penicillin.

"If you can get penicillin as a dry powder and keep it dry," he said, "it does not go bad. You can store it that way for weeks, months, maybe years."

In eight months the war was going badly. Belgium and Holland had fallen, and British troops were beginning the bloody evacuation from Dunkirk.

In the Oxford laboratories the penicillin hunters kept grimly on with their work. They had already checked every step of Fleming's earlier study and now were far beyond it; they had tested penicillin for toxicity on rats, mice, cats, and dogs, and even on the sensitive brain tissues of a rabbit without getting any signs of irritation; they had run series after series of test-tube experiments, finding exactly which microbes could be stopped by penicillin and which ones couldn't. And finally they had extracted enough moderately purified penicillin—a dirty brown powder—to try on microbes. Not microbes in a test tube this time, but germs rampaging through the blood and tissues of infected animals.

Florey sat in on that first animal test, the test which might brand these past months as a criminal waste of time. He watched eight sleek, healthy white mice taken from a cage and each given a huge injection of living, virulent microbes.

Four of those mice got nothing else. They were the controls, fated to die.

The other four got penicillin, injected every three hours, all night long.

"I must confess," he wrote afterward, "that it was one of the more exciting moments when we found in the morning that all the untreated mice were dead and all the penicillin-treated ones alive."

Penicillin had cured its first patients—four white mice.

With their tiny stock of penicillin, the scientists tried similar experiments and counted up at the end that the magic chemical had saved twenty-one out of twenty-four animals infected with streptococci, twenty-four out of twenty-five infected with a specially vicious strain of staphylococci, and twenty-four out of twenty-five infected with the gas-gangrene microbe.

In a brief report to the medical journal *Lancet* they wrote: "The results are clear cut. The antibacterial activity of penicillin is very great."

Now they wanted to go into the hospital wards, to try their brown powder on human patients, but there was no more penicillin—the mouse tests had taken it all. The men went back to work. Day by day, as the victorious Nazi armies swept across Europe and the threat of invasion came increasingly close to England, the Oxford scientists stuck to their benches. They poured more gallons of culture medium into their flasks and jars. They planted the mold again and again, tended it carefully as it grew, then drained off the broth and went through the long, tedious process of extraction. France collapsed, the Vichy government took over, and France broke off diplomatic relations with Britain.

Two months later the Luftwaffe opened the Battle of Britain, dropping terrible cascades of bombs each night on England's chief cities. At Oxford the chemists learned that penicillin is destroyed by contact with certain metals and they began to grow it in shallow, enamel-coated containers—hospital bedpans.

The Italians invaded Greece, and the British went on the offensive in North Africa and invaded Libya. At Oxford, Florey had put his entire department on penicillin. Now he was getting penicillin infinitely more pure than the earlier batches, and the power of this concentrated stuff was staggering—diluted a million to one it could still kill microbes!

Early in February of 1941, after nearly two years of hard work, the pile of penicillin seemed large enough to treat one human patient.

Dr. Charles Fletcher was selected to give the first treatment. When he took his vial of penicillin over to the Radcliffe Infirmary, the doctors there picked out their man—an Oxford policeman, forty-three years old, who had been in the hospital for four months. He had come in with a little sore at the corner of his mouth—a sore that stubbornly refused to heal and instead began to spread. Sulfa drugs did him no good; his was a breed of germs which were resistant to sulfas. Now he was dying from a combined staphylococcus and streptococcus infection of his face, scalp, both eyes, lungs, bones, and blood.

Fletcher examined the policeman. He was emaciated, moaning in pain, too weak even to lift an arm. He was coughing up pus. In spite of blood transfusions, his blood count was almost at rock bottom.

Fletcher took two hundred milligrams—less than one hundredth of an ounce—of his white power, dissolved it in water, sucked up the clear liquid in a syringe, and then injected it into the policeman's arm muscles. Three hours later he put a shot of one hundred milligrams into the policeman's veins. All through the day, every three hours, another tiny dose of penicillin was injected. After the first twelve hours the patient was still alive—but that was the best you could say.

"We'll keep it up all night, every three hours," Fletcher said.

The next day a nurse, hardly believing it herself, wrote on the policeman's chart: "Striking improvement."

The policeman was not merely alive—he was getting better! His temperature was down a little, his pain was disappearing, his lungs sounded better, and the laboratory sent back an encouraging report on his blood count. Here, for the first time, penicillin was bringing a man back from the grave.

It was a Wednesday when they started the treatment. By Friday, even the regular hospital doctor was beaming.

They were by no means through. The policeman was amazingly better, but he was not cured, and the little stockpile of penicillin was almost exhausted. The scientists rushed back to the patient's bedside. "Collect every ounce of this man's urine and send it over to the laboratory," they directed. "He's excreting a lot of penicillin through his kidneys. Maybe we can get some of it back."

Now they began a desperate attempt to get penicillin out of the policeman's urine, purify it, concentrate it again, and inject it back into him.

For a while this grotesque routine seemed to work. On Saturday the nurse jotted down again, "Continued improvement." On Sunday they had to interrupt treatment from noon to six o'clock at night until they could recapture more penicillin from the urine bottles, but the policeman was improving steadily, his blood count was climbing back, and one infected eye was practically normal.

On Monday the nurse greeted the doctors with cheering news. "He's much better this morning," she announced. "What about the injections today? Do we continue the usual . . ."

"No," said the doctors. "No injections today. We've run out of penicillin."

"But he's been doing so well! Can't you make some more?"

"It would take weeks, and he'll be dead by then."

He was.

"The attempt to treat this forlorn case was chiefly valuable in that it showed that penicillin could be given over a period of five days without significant toxic effect," Florey and his group reported. "Later experience showed that the dose of penicillin employed was too small, and the period of administration too short."

One vital lesson came out of the dramatic case of the dying policeman: *Give enough penicillin, and give it long enough, or you'll lose your patient.*

That lesson was underlined again a few weeks later when the Oxford workers had built up another small stock of penicillin and went back for their second patient. This time it was a fifteen-year-old youth who had come into the hospital for a bone operation, suffered a severe hemorrhage, and then came down with a rampaging infection. The doctors gave him sulfas, too, but they didn't help.

After five days of penicillin treatment, the patient was remarkably improved. Two ugly wounds on his hip were beginning to heal, color was coming back into his pale, hollow cheeks, and his temperature was normal.

But once more the penicillin ran out. After a few days the infection blazed again.

To some observers this entire penicillin research was a fantastic waste of men, money, and time. More than two full years had passed and not a single human life had been saved. Although the chemists had made one improvement after another, it was necessary to start with forty gallons of laboriously prepared "mold juice" and devote days of drudgery to extract enough penicillin to treat one patient for one day.

One expert, noting that the treatment in the first two cases had cost about a thousand dollars a day per patient, wrote: "At this moment, penicillin is to other antiseptics not unlike what radium is to other metals."

Under the inspiring leadership of Florey and Chain, however, the Oxford scientists refused to quit. Sooner or later, they were convinced, their luck would turn. Meanwhile, Florey brought in still more experts to speed the work; he got more money from the British Medical Research Council and the Rockefeller Foundation; and, of particular importance, he induced Imperial Chemical Industries, Ltd., to help make penicillin in their laboratories.

By May of 1941, with Greece and Yugoslavia conquered by the Germans and London taking the worst bombing raids of the war, the Oxford workers were ready to try once again. Their next patient was a forty-eight-year-old workman, a thin, broken-down little fellow who had just come into the hospital with a huge carbuncle that was pouring murderous staphylococci into his body. They were festering in his nose and his lungs, swelling the glands in his armpits, and sending his temperature higher every hour.

With penicillin for seven days, Fletcher cured him.

At long last penicillin had saved a human being.

The next patient, Number Four in the series, was another triumph for penicillin—but the patient died. He was a little four-year-old boy, semiconscious when brought to the hospital, his neck rigid, his eyes swollen, his spinal fluid swimming with staphylococci. Five weeks before he had come down with what appeared to be an ordinary case of measles, but the measles were followed by a minor skin infection, and this minor infection suddenly exploded into a general disease with germs spreading all over his body. In three days of penicillin treatment he was obviously better; in nine days he was talking and playing with his toys; but on the eighteenth day he died. Autopsy showed the penicillin had stopped the germs all right. Death had been caused by a ruptured blood vessel.

"Before this blood-vessel accident," Fletcher reported, "the patient had been restored from a dying condition to apparent convalescence." It was another pathetic case to lose.

From here on, however, the Oxford group began to click. They took a young woman whose vision was threatened by a horrible spreading ulcer and dropped penicillin into her eye hour after hour, saving her sight and possibly her life. They cured a terribly sick six-months-old baby, vomiting and feverish and shaken with convulsions, given up to die after sulfa drugs failed to stop a kidney infection. They saved a young boy dying from a staphylococcus infection of his blood stream and leg bones.

On August 16, 1941, Florey and his colleagues—all listed in alphabetical order—published the results on the first twelve patients under the title, "Further Observations on Penicillin." Their findings were unassailable: They had proved penicillin on human beings.

"I think the discovery and development of penicillin," said Florey, "may be looked on as quite one of the luckiest accidents that have occurred in medicine."

But there was still one huge hurdle to surmount. It had taken the Oxford workers more than two years to extract enough penicillin to treat twelve human beings, and there were patients by the tens of thousands whom it would unquestionably cure.

"We simply couldn't make enough of the stuff," one scientist declared. "We were being bombed, and most of our factories were all out to make things to hit the Germans. They couldn't give us sufficient aid."

Even before the report appeared in print, Florey called his shy assistant, Norman Heatley. "Pack up your things," he said. "We're going to America."

III

It is probable that sooner or later the Americans would have attempted to do something about this major problem of penicillin production. What made it much sooner was Hitler. When Florey and Heatley arrived in New York, five months before Pearl Harbor, they found that many Americans were already emotionally at war, already thinking about new war weapons and new drugs to save war wounded.

It was the fall of 1941 when America's production specialists
—chemists and bacteriologists and engineers—went to work on
penicillin. How much did they need? Nobody knew exactly, but
somebody suggested at least two pounds as a minimum for test
purposes.

How much might the job cost? Nobody knew that, either. If
they had realized then that eventually America and England
together would gamble nearly a hundred million dollars they
might never have started. All that anyone knew was that
penicillin—penicillin by the millions and millions of units—might
save a lot of lives.

For nearly a year the production crews sweated and strained.
They built great vats to grow mold; they tried scores and scores
of different mold foods; they developed dozens of methods to
extract the penicillin, to purify it, and to concentrate it. Thinking that they might find a more productive strain of mold lurk-
ing somewhere in the soil, the "mold merchants" asked the Army
Air Forces to bring back a sample of soil from every airfield in
the world. They tested every strain of mold that appeared on
old bread, old leather, and old cheese. But during that first year
the amount of penicillin they produced was pitiful, and all during that year civilian and military doctors pleaded for supplies.

Everything conspired to build up that demand. Florey's first
reports had opened the eyes of every British doctor, and the
British army, the navy, and the RAF put in immediate requisi-
tions. Civilian doctors called for penicillin to treat victims of
Nazi bombs. Even Alexander Fleming, still at St. Mary's Hospital in London, asked for a supply.

He called Florey at Oxford one day and said, "We've got a
man here with a streptococcus meningitis. Sulfa drugs don't do
him a bit of good. We started oxygen last night, but he's dying.
Do you have any spare penicillin?"

Fleming got his penicillin, injected it directly into the delicate lining of the spinal cord—the first time anyone had tried this with penicillin—and saved his patient's life. "Recovery was uninterrupted," he reported to Florey.

Fleming got a little bit of penicillin. Most doctors didn't, not in England nor in America, where another dramatic report—use of penicillin on victims of Boston's Cocoanut Grove fire—heightened the demand.

In 1943, however, things began happening on the production front. At Peoria, Robert Coghill and his men found two superior strains of mold; one had been there all the time in the laboratory's mold collection, and the other was found growing peacefully on a cantaloupe in a Peoria fruit market. Also, they took some corn-steep liquor—the fluid left over when corn is soaked in water during the manufacture of starch—and added it to the regular mold food; to their amazement it increased penicillin yield by ten times.

Production in January of 1943 was low—one hundred million units of penicillin, about two ounces, enough to treat perhaps a hundred and fifty men. By May the monthly output was up to four hundred and twenty-five million, by July it reached seven hundred and sixty-two million, and the "mold merchants" were beginning to hope that maybe they could meet the demand—but the demand went up, too.

British doctors reported additional hundreds of successful case histories—men, women, and children treated in civilian hospitals. Military doctors added more penicillin triumphs. Florey himself had spent the summer months in Algeria, testing penicillin on wounded men evacuated from the Battle of Sicily, with the temperature over ninety, clouds of dust from every passing vehicle sweeping over the cots, and swarms of flies settling on every exposed wound; even under these conditions, he announced, and even in the treatment of deadly brain infections, the action of penicillin was remarkable.

In August of 1943 American production climbed to nine hundred and six million units.

That month Dr. Chester S. Keefer of Boston reported the results of twenty-two American teams who had tested penicillin on five hundred closely watched patients. The results: three hundred and sixty-six recovered or improved, forty no effect, ninety-four deaths. It was the first major test of the drug in the United States. Keefer was the one man given the responsibility for deciding which patient should get penicillin and which should not. Deluged by a nationwide flood of pathetic requests from doctors and patients, he permitted the drug to be used only where it would add to medical knowledge. Time after time he was forced to turn down frantic pleas to save the lives of his friends and his friends' children.

It was also that month that Dr. Leo Loewe and his associates at the Jewish Hospital in Brooklyn succeeded for the first time in stopping one of the most devilish of all infections. This was subacute bacterial endocarditis, a bacterial infection of the heart valves, with a well-established mortality rate of 97 per cent. With penicillin, they reduced the rate to less than 20 per cent!

In September of 1943 production jumped to a billion seven hundred eighty-seven million units—two full pounds of penicillin, but that original goal had long since been expanded. American workers were now using penicillin to treat gonorrhea —reporting complete cures sometimes in forty-five hours.

In October John Mahoney and his men from the United States Public Health laboratories on Staten Island made the most exciting American contribution to the medical knowledge of penicillin. For years, seeking a better treatment for syphilis, they had routinely tried every new drug that appeared on the market. There was no reason why penicillin might have been expected to work, for the microbe of syphilis is no relative of the staphylococci or the streptococci or the pneumococci. But they tried penicillin anyhow, and penicillin *did* work!

Now the demand reached new peaks, but now the production men—the Peoria "mold merchants" and their industrial colleagues —were going high, wide, and handsome. Their huge vats, ten- and fifteen-thousand-gallon tanks, were pouring out penicillin. By the end of the war they were making a trillion units—more than a thousand pounds—a month. The battle of penicillin production had been won.

SURGICAL ADVENTURES

Rab and His Friends

by John Brown

The profession of surgery is as old as medicine itself. With an instrument startlingly similar to a carpenter's brace and bit, prehistoric peoples drilled holes into the skull, sometimes to relieve pressure caused by fractures, sometimes to make openings through which the spirits that had caused insanity could escape. Operations for cataract and rupture later became common. Saws, cleavers, and knives were used to sever arms and legs. Charlatans and quacks plied the trade. Barbers practiced it as a side line—hence the term "barber-surgeon." Physicians considered it disreputable.

Gradually, through the efforts of a group of brilliant men, the craft attained respectability. One of the first of these men was Ambroise Paré, a French physician of the sixteenth century. Paré, like many a surgeon who followed him, served his apprenticeship on the battlefield. Until his time gunshot wounds were first treated with boiling oil and then cauterized with red-hot irons to stop the bleeding. Paré eliminated both practices, treated the wounds with bland and soothing unguents, and "ligated" the bleeding blood vessels by tying them with pieces of twine, a practice that survives to the present day. "I dressed his wounds," said this gentle man, "and God healed him."

Yet in the very nature of things surgery remained the cruelest of the arts of healing. Operations were performed with incomplete knowledge of human anatomy and none whatever of anesthesia and antisepsis. In the primitive days before these discoveries, screaming sufferers were often held on the operating table by burly attendants, while surgeons, clad in filthy and bloodstained coats, performed their duties. The rudiments of cleanliness, even as performed by decent housewives, were not observed in the operating room.

Some descriptions of these early operations are horrifying in their gruesomeness. We have chosen "Rab and His Friends," not only because it is more quietly moving but also because it has historical importance. At the time of the story, John Brown was serving his surgical apprenticeship under James Syme, the noted Edinburgh physician who performed the operation described. Symes' older daughter later married Joseph Lister; and legend has it that a reading of "Rab and His Friends" so moved Lister that he was inspired, at least in part, to make his discovery of antisepsis.

Six years have passed—a long time for a boy and a dog. I am a medical student and clerk at Minto House Hospital.

Rab I saw almost every week, on the Wednesday; and we had much pleasant intimacy. I found the way to his heart by frequent scratching of his huge head and an occasional bone. When I did not notice him he would plant himself straight before me, and stand wagging that bud of a tail, and looking up, with his head a little to one side. His master I occasionally saw; he used to call me "Maister John," but was laconic as any Spartan.

One fine October afternoon I was leaving the hospital when I saw the large gate open, and in walked Rab, with that great and easy saunter of his. He looked as if taking general possession of the place; like the Duke of Wellington entering a subdued city, satiated with victory and peace. After him came Jess, now white with age, with her cart; and in it a woman, carefully wrapped up—the carrier leading the horse anxiously, and looking back. When he saw me, James (for his name was James Noble) made a curt and grotesque "boo," and said,

"Maister John, this is the mistress; she's got a trouble in her breest—some kind o' an income we're thinkin'."

By this time I saw the woman's face; she was sitting on a sack filled with straw, her husband's plaid round her, and his big coat, with its large white metal buttons, over her feet. I never saw a more unforgettable face—pale, serious, lonely,* delicate, sweet, without being what we call fine. She looked sixty, and had on a mutch, white as snow, with its black ribbon; her silvery smooth hair setting off her dark-gray eyes—eyes such as one sees only twice or thrice in a lifetime, full of suffering, but full also of the overcoming of it; her eyebrows black and delicate, and her mouth firm, patient, and contented, which few mouths ever are.

As I have said, I never saw a more beautiful countenance, or one more subdued to settled quiet. "Ailie," said James, "this is Maister John, the young doctor; Rab's friend, ye ken. We often speak about you, Doctor." She smiled, and made a movement, but said nothing; and prepared to come down, putting her plaid aside and rising. Had Solomon, in all his glory, been handing down the Queen of Sheba at his palace gate, he could not have done it more daintily, more tenderly, more like a gentleman, than did James the Howgate carrier when he lifted down Ailie, his wife. The contrast of his small, swarthy, weatherbeaten, keen, worldly face to hers—pale, subdued, and beautiful —was something wonderful. Rab looked on concerned and puzzled but ready for anything that might turn up—were it to strangle the nurse, the porter, or even me. Ailie and he seemed great friends.

"As I was sayin', she's got a kind o' trouble in her breest, Doctor; wull ye tak' a look at it?" We walked into the consult-

* It is not easy giving this look by one word; it was expressive of her being so much of her life alone.

ing room, all four; Rab grim and comic, willing to be happy
and confidential if cause could be shown, willing also to be quite
the reverse, on the same terms. Ailie sat down, undid her open
gown and her lawn handkerchief round her neck, and, without
a word, showed me her right breast. I looked at and examined
it carefully—she and James watching me, and Rab eying all
three. What could I say? There it was, that had once been so
soft, so shapely, so white, so gracious, and bountiful, "so full
of all blessed conditions"—hard as a stone, a center of horrid
pain, making that pale face, with its gray, lucid, reasonable
eyes and its sweet resolved mouth, express the full measure of
suffering overcome. Why was that gentle, modest, sweet woman,
clean and lovable, condemned by God to bear such a burden?

I got her away to bed. "May Rab and me bide?" said James.

"You may; and Rab, if he will behave himself."

"I'se warrant he's do that, Doctor"; and in slunk the faithful
beast. I wish you could have seen him. There are no such dogs
now: he belonged to a lost tribe. He was brindled, and gray like
Aberdeen granite; his hair short, hard, and close, like a lion's;
his body thickset, like a little bull—a sort of compressed Hercules
of a dog. He must have been ninety pounds' weight at the least;
he had a large blunt head; his muzzle black as night; his mouth
blacker than any night, a tooth or two—being all he had—
gleaming out of his jaws of darkness. His head was scarred
with the records of old wounds, a sort of series of fields of
battle all over it; one eye out; one ear cropped as close as was
Archbishop Leighton's father's—but for different reasons—the
remaining eye had the power of two; and above it, and in
constant communication with it, was a tattered rag of an ear,
which was forever unfurling itself, like an old flag; and then
that bud of a tail, about one inch long, if it could in any sense
be said to be long, being as broad as long—the mobility, the
instantaneousness of that bud was very funny and surprising,

and its expressive twinklings and winkings, the intercommunications between the eye, the ear, and it were of the subtlest and swiftest. Rab had the dignity and simplicity of great size; and having fought his way all along the road to absolute supremacy, he was as mighty in his own line as Julius Caesar or the Duke of Wellington; and he had the gravity† of all great fighters.

Next day my master, the surgeon, examined Ailie. There was no doubt it must kill her, and soon. It could be removed—it might never return—it would give her speedy relief—and she should have it done. She curtsied, looked at James, and said, "When?"

"Tomorrow," said the kind surgeon, a man of few words.

She and James and Rab and I retired. I noticed that he and she spoke little, but seemed to anticipate everything in each other.

The following day, at noon, the students came in, hurrying up the great stair. At the first landing place, on a small, well-known blackboard, was a bit of paper fastened by wafers, and many remains of old wafers beside it. On the paper were the words, "An operation today. J. B. Clerk."

Up ran the youths, eager to secure good places; in they crowded, full of interest and talk. "What's the case?" "Which side is it?"

Don't think them heartless; they are neither better nor worse than you or I: they get over their professional horrors and into their proper work; and in them pity—as an emotion, ending in itself or at best in tears and a long-drawn breath, lessens, while pity as a motive is quickened, and gains power and purpose. It is well for poor human nature that it is so.

† A Highland gamekeeper, when asked why a certain terrier, of singular pluck, was so much graver than the other dogs, said, "Oh, sir, life's full o' sairiousness to him—he just never can get enuff o' fechtin'."

The operating theater is crowded; much talk and fun, and all the cordiality and stir of youth. The surgeon with his staff of assistants is there. In comes Ailie; one look at her quiets and abates the eager students. That beautiful old woman is too much for them; they sit down, and are dumb, and gaze at her. These rough boys feel the power of her presence. She walks in quickly, but without haste; dressed in her mutch, her neckerchief, her white dimity shortgown, her black bombazeen petticoat, showing her white worsted stockings and her carpet shoes. Behind her was James, with Rab. James sat down in the distance, and took that huge and noble head between his knees. Rab looked perplexed and dangerous; forever cocking his ear and dropping it as fast.

Ailie stepped up on a seat, and laid herself on the table, as her friend the surgeon told her; arranged herself, gave a rapid look at James, shut her eyes, rested herself on me, and took my hand. The operation was at once begun; it was necessarily slow; and chloroform—one of God's best gifts to his suffering children— was then unknown. The surgeon did his work. The pale face showed its pain, but was still and silent. Rab's soul was working within him; he saw that something strange was going on—blood flowing from his mistress, and she suffering; his ragged ear was up, and importunate; he growled and gave now and then a sharp, impatient yelp; he would have liked to have done something to that man. But James had him firm, and gave him a glower from time to time and an intimation of a possible kick—all the better for James, it kept his eye and his mind off Ailie.

It is over: she is dressed, steps gently and decently down from the table, looks for James, then, turning to the surgeon and the students, she curtsies, and in a low, clear voice, begs their pardon if she has behaved ill. The students—all of us—wept like children; the surgeon wrapped her up carefully, and, resting on James and me, Ailie went to her room, Rab following. We put her to bed. James took off his heavy shoes, crammed with tackets, heel capped and toe capped, and put them carefully under the table, saying, "Maister John, I'm for nane o' yer strynge nurse bodies for Ailie. I'll be her nurse, and on my stockin' soles I'll gang about as canny as pussy." And so he did; and handy and clever, and swift and tender as any woman was that horny-handed, snell, peremptory little man. Everything she got he gave her: he seldom slept; and often I saw his small, shrewd eyes out of the darkness, fixed on her. As before, they spoke little.

Rab behaved well, never moving, showing us how meek and gentle he could be, and occasionally, in his sleep, letting us know that he was demolishing some adversary. He took a walk with me every day, generally to the Candlemaker Row; but he was somber and mild; declined doing battle, though some fit cases offered, and indeed submitted to sundry indignities; and was always very ready to turn, and came faster back, and trotted up the stair with much lightness, and went straight to that door.

Jess, the mare—now white—had been sent, with her weather-worn cart, to Howgate, and had doubtless her own dim and placid meditations and confusions on the absence of her master and Rab and her unnatural freedom from the road and her cart.

For some days Ailie did well. The wound healed "by the first intention"; as James said, "Oor Ailie's skin's ower clean to beil." The students came in quiet and anxious, and surrounded her bed. She said she liked to see their young, honest faces. The surgeon dressed her, and spoke to her in his own short, kind way, pitying her through his eyes. Rab and James outside the circle—Rab being now reconciled, and even cordial, and having made up his mind that as yet nobody required worrying, but, as you may suppose, *semper paratus*.

So far well: but four days after the operation my patient had a sudden and long shivering, a "groofin'," as she called it. I saw her soon after; her eyes were too bright, her cheek colored; she was

restless, and ashamed of being so; the balance was lost; mischief
had begun. On looking at the wound, a blush of red told the
secret: her pulse was rapid, her breathing anxious and quick, she
wasn't herself, as she said, and was vexed at her restlessness. We
tried what we could. James did everything, was everywhere;
never in the way, never out of it; Rab subsided under the table
into a dark place, and was motionless, all but his eye, which followed everyone. Ailie got worse; began to wander in her mind,
gently; was more demonstrative in her ways to James, rapid in
her questions, and sharp at times. He was vexed, and said, "She
was never that way afore; no, never." For a time she knew her
head was wrong, and was always asking our pardon—the dear,
gentle old woman: then delirium set in strong, without pause.
Her brain gave way, and that terrible spectacle,

> "The intellectual power, through words and things,
>   Went sounding on its dim and perilous way;"

she sang bits of old songs and Psalms, stopping suddenly, min-
gling the Psalms of David, and the diviner words of his Son and
Lord, with homely odds and ends and scraps of ballads.

Nothing more touching, or in a sense more strangely beautiful,
did I ever witness. Her tremulous, rapid, affectionate, eager
Scotch voice—the swift, aimless, bewildered mind, the baffled
utterance, the bright and perilous eye; some wild words, some
household cares, something for James, the names of the dead,
Rab called rapidly and in a "fremyt" voice, and he starting up,
surprised, and slinking off as if he were to blame somehow, or
had been dreaming he heard. Many eager questions and beseech-
ings which James and I could make nothing of, and on which she
seemed to set her all and then sink back ununderstood. It was
very sad, but better than many things that are not called sad.
James hovered about, put out and miserable, but active and exact

as ever; read to her, when there was a lull, short bits from the Psalms, prose and meter, changing the latter in his own rude and serious way, showing great knowledge of the fit words, bearing up like a man, and doting over her as his "ain Ailie." "Ailie, ma woman!" "Ma ain bonnie wee dawtie!"

The end was drawing on: the golden bowl was breaking; the silver cord was fast being loosed—that *animula, blandula, vagula, hospes, comesque* was about to flee. The body and the soul—companions for sixty years—were being sundered, and taking leave. She was walking, alone, through the valley of that shadow into which one day we must all enter—and yet she was not alone, for we know whose rod and staff were comforting her.

One night she had fallen quiet, and, as we hoped, asleep; her eyes were shut. We put down the gas, and sat watching her. Suddenly she sat up in bed, and taking a bed gown which was lying on it rolled up, she held it eagerly to her breast, to the right side. We could see her eyes bright with a surprising tenderness and joy, bending over this bundle of clothes. She held it as a woman holds her sucking child; opening out her nightgown impatiently, and holding it close, and brooding over it, and murmuring foolish little words, as over one whom his mother comforteth, and who is sucking, and being satisfied. It was pitiful and strange to see her wasted dying look, keen and yet vague—her immense love. "Preserve me!" groaned James, giving way. And then she rocked back and forward, as if to make it sleep, hushing it, and wasting on it her infinite fondness. "Wae's me, Doctor: I declare she's thinkin' it's that bairn."

"What bairn?"

"The only bairn we ever had; our wee Mysie, and she's in the Kingdom forty years and mair." It was plainly true: the pain in the breast, telling its urgent story to a bewildered, ruined brain; it was misread and mistaken; it suggested to her the uneasiness of a breast full of milk, and then the child; and so again once more they were together, and she had her ain wee Mysie in her bosom. This was the close. She sank rapidly; the delirium left her; but as she whispered, she was clean silly; it was the lightening before the final darkness. After having for some time lain still, her eyes shut, she said "James!" He came close to her, and lifting up her calm, clear, beautiful eyes, she gave him a long look, turned to me kindly but shortly, looked for Rab but could not see him, then turned to her husband again, as if she would never leave off looking, shut her eyes, and composed herself. She lay for some time breathing quick, and passed away so gently that when we thought she was gone, James, in his old-fashioned way, held the mirror to her face. After a long pause one small spot of dimness was breathed out; it vanished away, and never returned, leaving the blank, clear darkness of the mirror without a stain. "What is our life? It is even a vapor, which appeareth for a little time, and then vanisheth away."

Rab all this time had been full awake and motionless; he came forward beside us. Ailie's hand, which James had held, was hanging down; it was soaked with his tears; Rab licked it all over carefully, looked at her, and returned to his place under the table.

James and I sat, I don't know how long, but for some time, saying nothing. He started up abruptly, and with some noise went to the table, and putting his right fore and middle fingers each into a shoe, pulled them out, and put them on, breaking one of the leather latchets, and muttering in anger, "I never did the like o' that afore!"

I believe he never did; nor after either. "Rab!" he said roughly, and pointing with his thumb to the bottom of the bed. Rab leaped up, and settled himself, his head and eye to the dead face. "Maister John, ye'll wait for me," said the carrier, and disappeared in the darkness, thundering downstairs in his heavy shoes. I ran to a front window; there he was, already round the house, and out at the gate, fleeing like a shadow.

I was afraid about him, and yet not afraid; so I sat down beside Rab, and being wearied, fell asleep. I woke from a sudden noise outside. It was November, and there had been a heavy fall of snow. Rab was in *status quo;* he heard the noise, too, and plainly knew it, but never moved. I looked out; and there, at the gate, in the dim morning—for the sun was not up—was Jess and the cart—a cloud of steam rising from the old mare. I did not see James; he was already at the door, and came up the stairs, and met me. It was less than three hours since he left, and he must have posted out—who knows how?—to Howgate, full nine miles off, yoked Jess, and driven her astonished into town. He had an armful of blankets, and was streaming with perspiration. He nodded to me, spread out on the floor two pairs of old clean blankets, having at their corners, "A.G., 1794," in large letters in red worsted. These were the initials of Alison Graeme, and James may have looked in at her from without—unseen but not unthought of—when he was "wat, wat, and weary," and had walked many a mile over the hills, and seen her sitting, while "a' the lave were sleepin' "; and by the firelight putting her name on the blankets for her ain James's bed. He motioned Rab down, and taking his wife in his arms, laid her in the blankets, and wrapped her carefully and firmly up, leaving the face uncovered; and then lifting her, he nodded again sharply to me, and with a resolved but utterly miserable face, strode along the passage, and downstairs, followed by Rab. I also followed, with a light; but he didn't need it. I went out, holding stupidly the light in my hand in the frosty air. We were soon at the gate. I could have helped him, but I saw he was not to be meddled with, and he was strong, and did not need it. He laid her down as tenderly, as safely, as he had lifted her out ten days before—as tenderly as when he had her first in his arms when she was only "A.G."—sorted her, leaving that beautiful sealed face open to the heavens, and then taking Jess by the head, he moved away. He did not

notice me, neither did Rab, who presided along behind the cart.
I stood till they passed through the long shadow of the college
and turned up Nicolson Street. I heard the solitary cart sound
through the streets, and die away and come again; and I returned,
thinking of that company going up Liberton brae, then along
Roslin muir, the morning light touching the Pentlands and making them like onlooking ghosts; then down the hill through
Auchindinny woods, past "haunted Woodhouselee"; and as day-
break came sweeping up the bleak Lammermuirs, and fell on his
own door, the company would stop, and James would take the
key, and lift Ailie up again, laying her on her own bed, and,
having put Jess up, would return with Rab and shut the door.

James buried his wife, with his neighbors mourning, Rab in-
specting the solemnity from a distance. It was snowing, and that
black ragged hole would look strange in the midst of the swelling
spotless cushion of white. James looked after everything; then
rather suddenly fell ill, and took to bed; was insensible when the
doctor came, and soon died. A sort of low fever was prevailing
in the village, and his want of sleep, his exhaustion, and his misery
made him apt to take it. The grave was not difficult to reopen.
A fresh fall of snow had again made all things white and smooth;
Rab once more looked on and slunk home to the stable.

And what of Rab? I asked for him next week at the new
carrier's who got the good will of James's business, and was now
master of Jess and her cart.

"How's Rab?"

He put me off and said rather rudely, "What's your business
wi' the dowg?"

I was not to be so put off. "Where's Rab?"

He, getting confused and red, and intermeddling with his hair,
said, "Deed, sir, Rab's died."

"Dead! What did he die of?"

"Weel, sir," said he, getting redder, "he didna exactly die; he

was killed. I had to brain him wi' a rack pin; there was nae doin'
wi' him. He lay in the treviss wi' the mear, and wadna come oot.
I tempit him wi' kail and meat, but he wad tak' naething, and
keepit me frae feedin' the beast, and he was aye gur gurrin', and
grup gruppin' me by the legs. I was laith to mak' awa wi' the
auld dowg, but his like wasna atween this and Thornill—but
'deed, sir, I could do naething else." I believed him. Fit end for
Rab, quick and complete. His teeth and his friends gone, why
should he keep the peace and be civil?

Victory Over Pain

by Victor Robinson

We now come to the first of two great discoveries which have saved millions of human beings from suffering and made surgery a blessing rather than a curse. Before anesthesia operations were resorted to only when all other cures had failed. They were performed under conditions utterly unlike those of today. Speed, for example, was one of the essentials. It was said of some of the most skillful surgeons that they could remove an arm or a leg in the twinkling of an eye, and that the observer who turned aside to sneeze might miss the entire operation. Only work of the crudest sort could be performed under such conditions. The slow, careful probing of the human body which is now so common and which often lasts for hours was impossible without the use of anesthesia and its sister discovery antisepsis. It is ironical that the story of this boon to humanity is filled with scenes of the grossest self-seeking and that it resulted only in tragedy for most of those who had a part in it.

Crawford Williamson Long

Despite Puritan opposition, the nomadic circus early became a feature of American life. Among the traveling showmen of the 1830's, none was more picturesque than a tall lad in a frock coat and a high hat, advertising himself—at the tender age of eighteen —as "Dr. Coult of New York, London, and Calcutta." Actually, he was Samuel Colt of Hartford, Connecticut, and his formal education was limited to an unfinished course in a preparatory school. Young Sam Colt was going around the country giving exhibitions of nitrous oxide (laughing gas) to obtain the cash he needed to patent his revolver—the revolver which bears his name and brought him fame and fortune.

Sam made as much as ten dollars a day in this homely manner. It is not surprising that a year or two later, when he needed money for the Canadian patents on his weapon, he bethought himself of laughing gas as a quick source of ready funds. At this time he lived in Cincinnati, where he was part owner of the Penny Museum. His showmanship had grown with his still-tender years, and he hired six Indians to appear in a gas-inspired comedy.

The place was crowded with curious citizens on the evening of the first performance. But nobody, least of all Sam Colt, was prepared for what actually did happen. The inventor of the revolver administered the gas to his six red Indians—who promptly fell sound asleep with not so much as a preliminary whoop or a drunken giggle. Sam knew very well that his customers had not paid their admission to see Indians taking a nap. He saved the day by administering the gas to a blacksmith who obliged by furiously chasing Sam about the stage. He finally careened into the seated Indians who woke to find themselves on the floor.

The audience applauded what they thought had been a planned act. But Sam Colt could find no answer to the puzzle, and he knew his show had come close to a fiasco. He abandoned his laughing-gas demonstrations.

It is very curious to see how this acutely alert New England lad, so alive to new ideas, had failed to notice the extraordinary fact that he had produced complete anesthesia.

The scene now shifts to the sleepy southern town of Jefferson, Georgia, a typical antebellum agricultural community. Even before Samuel Colt had given his Cincinnati demonstration of the effects of nitrous oxide, the boys and girls of many small towns were familiar with laughing gas as an excitant.

The town physician of Jefferson was one Crawford Williamson Long, who had four students in his office. Long's students were familiar with the effects of nitrous oxide from the parties they had attended. No doubt they had also seen the itinerant lecturers who traveled the country expounding the marvels of chemistry and generally winding up with a demonstration of the exhilarating properties of laughing gas.

Long was only twenty-seven years of age, his pupils between nineteen and twenty-one. The doctor entered into the sports of his students heartily, without neglecting in the least his duties as their teacher. On one occasion, when Long's boys were discussing the amazing antics of people under the influence of the gas, they asked him to make them some. In those easygoing times the town physician was also the local druggist-chemist, and the request was a natural one. This occasion is best described in Long's own account of those momentous years:

In the month of December, 1841, or January, 1842, the subject of the inhalation of nitrous oxide was introduced in a company of young men assembled at night in this village (Jefferson) and several persons present desired me to prepare some for their use. I informed them that I had no apparatus for preparing or preserving the gas, but that I had a medicine (sulfuric ether) which would produce equally exhilarating effects; that I had inhaled it myself, and considered it as safe as the nitrous oxide. One of the company stated that he had inhaled ether while at school, and was then willing to inhale it. The company were all anxious to witness its effects. I gave it first to the gentleman who had previously inhaled it, then inhaled it myself, and afterwards gave it to all persons present. They were so much pleased with the exhilarating effects of ether that they afterward inhaled it frequently, and induced others to do so, and its inhalation soon became quite fashionable in this country, and in fact extended from this place through several counties in this part of Georgia.

He himself became furiously excited on several occasions after inhaling the vapor and could not control his movements. When he emerged from the ether intoxication, as he called it, he would find that his arms and hands were severely bruised. Yet he had not been conscious of feeling any pain. He saw that his friends, while etherized, often fell to the floor with a thud that should have hurt them badly. When he questioned them, they agreed uniformly that they had not felt the least effect.

Among Long's patients was a young man named James M. Venable who had two tumors on the back of his neck. Venable was a local resident who was fond of ether and, like many of the other villagers, accustomed to inhaling it.

It was about James M. Venable that the first use of ether and the first instance of complete anesthesia induced by it were recorded; and it was Long who administered it and performed the excision of the tumorous growths on March 30, 1842. But strange to relate, Long appeared to have been utterly unaware of the significance of this great event, and did nothing to announce his discovery.

In his ledger occurs the simple entry: "James Venable, 1842. Ether and excising tumor, $2.00."

In his own behalf Long said:

> I was anxious, before making my publication, to try etherization in a sufficient number of cases to fully satisfy my mind that anesthesia was produced by the ether, and was not the effect of the imagination, or owing to any peculiar insusceptibility to pain in the person experimented upon . . . I determined to wait . . . to see whether any surgeon would present a claim to having used ether by inhalation in surgical operations prior to the time it was used by me.

By delaying publication Long lost the honor he might have won. From him cannot be withheld the credit of prior experiment and discovery; but to him cannot be granted the credit for influencing the historical development of anesthesia or giving it to the world.

With the advent of civil conflict, Long joined the Confederate Army and was given charge of a hospital on the campus of the university at Athens. During his flight before the oncoming Union forces in 1864 he carried with him a glass jar containing a roll of papers—"my proofs of the discovery of ether anesthesia."

Ten years later, struggling with the difficulties of bad times and a heavy but unremunerative practice, Long was still in harness. Attending a woman in labor, he administered ether. When his patient was fully anesthetized, he delivered the child. At the very moment he handed the baby to a nurse he had an apoplectic stroke and fell unconscious. He was carried into another room and died a few hours later; the date was June 16, 1878.

Long was sixty-two years of age when death took him. His life, which might have been bright with accomplishment, was ill-starred with disappointment and final poverty. But he died practicing his profession. Most fitting was his last act—the use of ether to relieve the pains of childbirth.

Horace Wells

The time is 1844. A favorite diversion was the lecture on the marvels of chemistry, ending with demonstrations of the effect of laughing gas.

The street-corner professors, the tent-show exhibitors of chemical wonders, doubtless attracted their audiences in the fashion so typically Yankee which we still know in the carnivals of today.

HUR-RY, HUR-RY, HUR-RY! SEE the great exhibition of the gas that MAKES you laugh! FEEL the pleasurable sensations that

rouse the risibilities. This MARVELOUS VAPOR excites every
fiber of the body to ACTION and sharpens all the faculties of
the MIND. STEP RIGHT UP, GET YOUR TICKETS HERE!

One of these showmen, though his lecture was given in the
respectable theaters and halls of the larger towns, was Gardner
Quincy Colton. Colton's wits were sharpened by years of hand-
to-mouth existence. It occurred to him to dignify the catchpenny
demonstrations of the itinerant workers of chemical wonders.
He proposed to friends that they furnish the money for leasing a
hall where, posing as "Professor" Colton, he would give a frock-
coated exhibition of chemical marvels and induce the audience to
try nitrous oxide after he had described its amusing effects.

To the astonishment of Colton's friends, the lecture was a
resounding success. A large audience paid the amazing total of
$535 to witness the performance. Fortune beckoned: Gardner
Colton made arrangements to repeat his success.

On December 10, 1844, he gave his show in Hartford, Connecticut. The occasion is famous today for the presence there of
Horace Wells.

Colton's own account of what happened vividly brings to life
this colorful, historic figure. Although other witnesses of this
interesting and important occasion will be needed to round out
fully our description of it, the warm and generous Colton has
richly earned his opportunity to speak:

> On the 10th of December, 1844, I gave an exhibition of
> laughing gas in the city of Hartford, Connecticut. After a
> brief lecture on the properties and effects of the gas, I in-
> vited a dozen or fifteen gentlemen to come up on the stage
> who would like to inhale it. Among those who came for-
> ward was Dr. Horace Wells, a dentist of Hartford, and a
> young man by the name of Cooley.
> Cooley inhaled the gas, and while under its influence ran
> against some wooden settees on the stage and bruised his legs

badly. On taking his seat next to Dr. Wells, the latter said to him, "You must have hurt yourself." "No." Then he began to feel some pain, and was astonished to find his legs bloody; he said he felt no pain till the effects of the gas had passed off.

At the close of the exhibition Dr. Wells came to me, and said, "Why cannot a man have a tooth extracted under the gas, and not feel it?"

I replied I did not know.

Dr. Wells then said he believed it could be done, and would try it on himself, if I would bring a bag of gas to his office. The next day—11th of December, 1844—I went to his office with a bag of gas.

It is very important for our story to note that Colton always gave credit to Horace Wells for suggesting the first practical use of nitrous oxide.

When Wells made his wonderful discovery that the extraction of teeth could be freed from pain, the event brought stark tragedy to himself and his entire family. His widow later declared that the discovery "has been to her family an unspeakable evil." It cost the life of her husband and substituted domestic conflict for what had been a lucrative professional life and a happy home.

Wells was born January 21, 1815, at Hartford, Vermont. His parents were intelligent, wealthy for that region, and very indulgent. The boy was bright, and they made certain that he lacked for no comforts or advantages which they were able to give him.

In the year 1834, when he was nineteen, he began the study of dentistry in Boston. Dental colleges had not yet been established but Wells received the best education possible at the time. He read under preceptors and acquired clinical experience in the office of the best practitioners. He quickly made a place for himself in a city widely celebrated for the skill of its dental surgeons.

He, too, soon accepted students. Among them was John Mankey Riggs, of Hartford, after whom Riggs' disease (alveolar pyorrhea) was later to be named, and William T. G. Morton, of Boston. Both of these pupils figure prominently in our story. It was Riggs who earned the honor of extracting the first tooth without pain, performing the operation at Wells's request.

It happened that Wells had a troublesome wisdom tooth; he decided to submit to the operation himself if Riggs would perform it.

Early the next morning Wells called for Colton. The "professor" brought with him a supply of the gas in a rubber container equipped with tubing and a wooden spigot. With one of Colton's brothers, who was making the tour with the "professor," they proceeded to Wells's office. There Riggs awaited them, as well as Cooley, whose battered legs of the night before had set Wells on the path he was now following.

Wells seated himself in his own operating chair. He took into his mouth the rubber tube that Colton handed him, and the lecturer opened the spigot. Riggs waited until Colton, who gave a little more of the gas than he usually administered at his demonstrations, signified that Wells was apparently "under." Riggs picked up his forceps. Firmly, while casting an anxious eye on the strangely quiescent Wells, he gripped the root, rocking it to break it loose, and pulled. He held the bloody molar in the air while Wells did not even stir in his seat. There was no sign of any reaction whatever. Colton, Riggs, and Cooley exchanged glances. There was no doubt in their keen Yankee minds that they were in the presence of something of transcending significance.

Tranquilly, Wells regained consciousness. Riggs showed him the tooth, still gripped in the forceps. Wells exclaimed, "It is the greatest discovery ever made; I did not feel it so much as the prick of a pin!"

That was the first tooth ever drawn under the influence of total anesthesia, or at any rate the first reliably recorded instance of it. Wells and Riggs were intensely excited. Wells promptly obtained Colton's agreement to show him all he knew about the preparation of nitrous oxide and the laboratory apparatus that would be needed.

Colton's demonstration had taken place December 10, 1844. On the very next day Wells had made the first experiment—with himself as guinea pig. After assembling the materials that were needed to manufacture the gas, Wells instantly sought a score of opportunities to employ it. The entire period of discovery, manufacture, and further testing could not have been more than a fortnight in duration. Early in January Wells presented himself at Boston to his old student, William T. G. Morton. He told Morton the exciting news.

An acquaintance of both Morton and Wells was the eminent chemist and geologist Charles T. Jackson, who had once rented Morton an office when he first struck out for himself. Morton, who knew Wells's quality, was inclined to take the idea very seriously, but Jackson pooh-poohed it. Major surgical operations without pain! Utterly preposterous!

This was the reaction of a man who was to have an important influence upon the final acceptance of anesthesia, a man who was also to become one of the embittered claimants to its discovery.

Jackson doubtless considered that the findings of a dentist could scarcely be worthy of his own serious attention. But Morton had connections at the Massachusetts General Hospital and Wells persuaded him to help obtain a hearing. Colton's account of this portion of Wells's trials is unusually interesting.

"At length," Colton wrote in his defense of Wells, "he went to Cambridge College, and the elder Dr. John Collins Warren, at the close of his lecture on surgery, said to the class, 'There is a gentleman here who pretends he has got something which will destroy pain in a surgical operation. He wants to address you. If any of you would like to hear him, you can do so.' "

Wells made a few brief statements to his audience—Morton was present but Jackson was not—and then, as some accounts have it, he asked for a volunteer on whom to demonstrate. He administered the gas to his patient, applied his instrument, and proceeded to extract the tooth. Whether he had not waited long enough for the vapor to take effect, had given an inadequate quantity of gas, or whether the patient moaned even though anesthesia was complete, will remain a mystery.

At the last moment, just as Wells drew the tooth, the boy in the chair made a sharp outcry. The students jeered, hissed, and shouted "Humbug!" Wells was driven from the hospital amphitheater a dejected figure, his head bowed, his eyes unseeing.

Although he returned to Hartford dismayed at his luckless inability to persuade the doctors that surgical operations could be performed painlessly, he still believed in the discovery he had fathered, since he continued to administer nitrous oxide to his own patients. Bishop Brownell, his two daughters, and some forty citizens of Hartford later gave sworn depositions that during 1845 Wells extracted teeth for them without pain, using the gas as an anesthetic.

Meanwhile, in 1846, the first printed claims to Wells's discovery of anesthesia appeared in the December 7 edition of the Hartford *Courant*. This was a month after Morton's results had been published by Henry J. Bigelow in the issue of the *Boston Medical and Surgical Journal* dated November 18, 1846.

Wells's health began to decline. With the seeds of conflict among Morton, Jackson, and himself already well sown, Wells decided upon a change of scene. Early in 1847 he sailed for Paris. There he made the acquaintance of an American dentist, C. Starr Brewster. Brewster was much interested in Wells's story of what had taken place. He brought Wells's case before several French learned societies although the Paris Medical Institute had already granted, somewhat precipitately, 2,500 francs and its recognition to Charles T. Jackson for the discovery of the principle of anesthesia, and the same sum to Morton for his work in the discovery's application.

Wells published a letter, dated February 17, 1847, in *Galignani's Messenger*, stating his claims to priority over both Jackson and Morton, and declaring he had used ether as well as nitrous oxide. His story was viewed with widespread sympathy. He was lionized at parties and fetes, hailed everywhere as a hero.

On his return to America he found that other developments had taken place which cast a deeper shadow over his accomplishments. The tide of influence had turned completely in favor of the use of sulfuric ether. Nitrous oxide and its first proponent were all but forgotten.

Morton and Jackson were squabbling viciously over which of them should receive the credit for ether's introduction. And chloroform, meanwhile, had been brought forward by James Young Simpson of Scotland, and bade fair to challenge ether as a general anesthetic.

The rival claims of Morton and Jackson preyed horribly upon Wells's mind. His pioneering was all but forgotten. His years of experimentation with the gas had undermined him. Tests of the efficacy of chloroform, to which he devoted himself, produced a complete collapse.

On January 24, 1848, he anesthetized himself with the chloroform he had been inhaling. In the last conscious second before he succumbed to its influence, he slashed the femoral artery of his thigh with a razor.

Twelve days earlier a letter addressed to Wells had been posted in Paris. Transportation was slow in that day and Horace Wells was never to read:

My Dear Wells:

I have just returned from a meeting of the Paris Medical Society, where they have voted that to Horace Wells, of Hartford, Connecticut, United States of America, is due all the honor of having successfully discovered and successfully applied the use of vapors or gases whereby surgical operations could be performed without pain. They have done even more, for they have elected you honorary member of their Society. This was the third meeting that the Society had deliberated on the subject. On the two previous occasions, Mr. Warren, the agent of Dr. Morton, was present and endeavored to show that to his client was due the honor but he, having completely failed, did not attend the last meeting. The use of ether took the place of nitrous oxide gas, but chloroform has supplanted both, yet the first person, who first discovered and performed surgical operations without pain, was Horace Wells, and to the last day of time must suffering humanity bless his name.

Your diploma and the vote of the Paris Medical Society shall be forwarded to you. In the interim, you may use this letter as you please.

Believe me ever truly yours,

Brewster

Charles Thomas Jackson

Charles Thomas Jackson was a bizarre character. And if there was one thing that could easily be foretold of this eccentric man of science, it was that he would lay claim, like a scientific octopus, to any new developments that showed themselves within his reach.

Jackson suggested the use of ether to Morton, its first demonstrator. But upon witnessing Morton's extraordinary success and seeing him hailed as a great benefactor, Jackson was gnawed by a savage jealousy which drove him, true to form, to claim the triumph for himself.

Jackson had also made a characteristic effort to obtain for himself the glory of William Beaumont. The year was 1834. Beaumont was a military surgeon who, through the famous gunshot accident to Alexis St. Martin which left a "window" in the young French-Canadian's stomach, made the first great researches on the processes of digestion.

Beaumont toured with St. Martin, exhibiting him before various medical societies, and left some gastric fluid with Jackson, in Boston, for a chemical analysis of its properties. Jackson soon used up his supply, and learned, to his dismay, that Beaumont had been ordered to the West, making St. Martin no longer available for further experimentation, on which Jackson had become keenly intent.

The incredible Jackson vigorously set about forestalling their departure. He caused a petition to be circulated among the members of Congress, more than two hundred of whom willingly signed it. The petition was presented by Edward Everett to the Secretary of War just as Beaumont started for his new post under military orders.

It is well-nigh unbelievable that Jackson had never consulted Beaumont as to his wishes on the subject. In the light of Jackson's later behavior, of which this is the first striking example, one may be sure that if the request had been granted Jackson would have claimed for himself Beaumont's discoveries in physiology. And these experiments of Beaumont were not to be surpassed until the close of the century, with the work in Russia of Pavlov and his pupils.

In 1846, the year Jackson "discovered" anesthesia, he was also to claim the prior discovery of gun cotton after it had been announced by C. F. Schönbein.*

On September 30, 1846, Jackson suggested to Morton that he

* He also claimed that he, and not Samuel F. B. Morse, had invented the telegraph.—Eds.

use ether in extracting a tooth, and told him how to administer it. There is almost no objective evidence that Morton was merely acting as Jackson's "agent," as Jackson later declared brazenly, or that he was exploiting Morton merely as a tool in "a series of experiments," or that Jackson had any notion whatever of the true scope of Morton's information on ether or his plans for using it as an anesthetic.

Jackson was not present at Morton's famous demonstration of ether's use in surgery, nor did Jackson take any interest in the rapid developments that immediately followed Morton's success.

But then the roar of acclaim for Morton reached Jackson's ears. Among those who hailed Morton was Oliver Wendell Holmes, whose letter is worth quoting:

> November 21, 1846
> My Dear Sir:
> Everybody wants to have a hand in the great discovery. All I will do is give you a hint or two as to names, or the name, to be applied to the state produced, and to the agent.
> The state should, I think, be called *anesthesia*. . . . The adjective will be *anesthetic*.

This and other signals of Morton's overnight triumph were more than Jackson could bear. On December 21, 1846, he addressed two letters to his old friend, L. Élie de Beaumont. He requested that they be read to the French Academy of Sciences, and without so much as mentioning the name of Morton, he announced himself as the discoverer of surgical anesthesia.

On March 2, 1847, he read a paper to the American Academy of Arts and Sciences in which he first publicly proclaimed himself as ether's discoverer. This brief paper Jackson caused to be printed in the Boston *Daily Advertiser* of the day before so that he could send copies abroad on the March 1 mail packet. The effect of this action was to make it appear that the Academy had actually given its endorsement to Jackson's claim. The impression prevailed in Europe for a considerable time thereafter, even though the Academy did everything it could to counteract Jackson's stratagem.

The remainder of Jackson's career is a compound of excursions to Congress, either to obtain recognition for himself or to prevent it for Morton; of commissions to assay mining properties; of routine laboratory work; and writing. In 1861 he published his *Manual of Etherization* which, curiously enough, contained researches Jackson claimed to have made on the use of ether in cases of insanity. One of these cases was conducted at the McLean Asylum, a department of Massachusetts General Hospital. Twelve years later McLean was to admit another patient, a man who had performed scientific researches there, who had attended lectures within the walls of the hospital of which it formed a part. His name was Charles Thomas Jackson. He was to spend the last seven years of his life at the asylum. No record exists that the gas whose discovery as an anesthetic he claimed, and with whose use in insanity he experimented, was used in his own case or had any value if it was actually employed. He died there on August 28, 1880.

William Thomas Green Morton

At nine o'clock on the evening of September 30, 1846, an event of the greatest significance occurred in the office of William Thomas Green Morton, a Boston dentist. On this early fall evening, well past the time when a patient could be expected, Morton's aide, a Dr. Hayden, answered a knock at the door. He admitted Mr. Eben H. Frost who had been suffering from a terrible toothache for several days, and had finally decided that the torture of an extraction was preferable to another sleepless

night. Hayden conducted Frost to Morton's operating chair and
the patient seated himself nervously.

"Doctor," he said, "can't you give me something for this
tooth? How about this mesmerizing I've been reading about?"

Here was just the man Morton had been waiting for.

"I have something much better than that," he said. He called
his assistant. "Hayden! Bring the lamp."

It was now quite dark. Morton needed a good light to see what
he was doing. He took out a container of rectified ether he had
purchased a few days earlier from Joseph Burnett, the apothecary to whom he had gone at the suggestion of Charles T.
Jackson. Carefully he poured the fluid on a folded pocket handkerchief and gave it to the trembling Frost to hold beneath his
nose. Frost inhaled almost greedily. In less than a minute his hand
dropped into his lap. He slept.

Morton worked with a speed acquired from countless extractions where the faster the dentist worked, the less pain the
patient felt. Hayden held the lamp close to Frost's yawning
mouth. The gods of chance were with Morton. The highly in-
flammable ether fumes did not ignite as they well might have.
Morton gripped the abscessed bicuspid with his forceps. The
patient did not so much as stir. Morton yanked. The tooth was
in the air, but still the patient slept and showed no sign of pain.
Morton exchanged a look of utter triumph with Hayden.

Morton was no fool. He promptly obtained from Frost this
certificate, which he doubtless wrote himself for Frost's signa-
ture:

This is to certify that I applied to Dr. Morton, at 9
o'clock this evening, suffering under the most violent toothache; that Dr. Morton took out his pocket handkerchief,
saturated it with a preparation of his, from which I breathed
for about half a minute, and then was lost in sleep. In an

instant I awoke, and saw my tooth lying on the floor. I did not experience the slightest pain whatever. I remained twenty minutes in his office afterward, and felt no unpleasant effects from the operation.

Morton was practical, and a practical man does not let a matter like this drop after having gone so far. The next day, October 1, 1846, there appeared in the Boston *Daily Journal* the following advice:

> Last evening, as we were informed by a gentleman who witnessed the operation, an ulcerated tooth was extracted from the mouth of an individual, without giving the slightest pain. He was put into a kind of sleep, by inhaling a preparation, the effects of which lasted for about three quarters of a minute, just long enough to extract the tooth.

Although Morton later professed that the newspaper had somehow got this information without his knowledge, there is more than a little reason to believe that the *Journal's* informant was none other than the good doctor himself.

How long Morton had been experimenting with ether is a matter of question. That he was a witness to Wells's experiments with nitrous oxide the reader knows. And that Jackson contributed the suggestion that ether be used instead of laughing gas, and a purified ether at that, has also been established.

The question raised so often is: if Morton had been using ether in certain trials himself, why did he pretend ignorance of it when Jackson casually recommended it? Morton, the man of business, was on the trail of something he knew would be a money-maker and a patient getter. Jackson's reputation, which had certainly begun to tarnish as a result of his claim to Morse's telegraph, his attempt to detain St. Martin, and his assertion that he was the prior discoverer of Schönbein's collodion, would not have seemed conducive to any confidences of Morton's. So the dentist, whose knowledge of chemistry was sketchy, cannily pumped Jackson.

Morton took the essentially businesslike precaution of revealing the nature of his "preparation" to no one. Energetically he set about capitalizing on the *Journal* story of October 1. A bit of judicious word-of-mouth advertising spread the news that William Thomas Green Morton was the dentist who made tooth pulling painless. The patients began to come. Within the next few days he had at least four or five opportunities, perhaps more, to test ether. In one instance it produced nothing but a protracted vomiting spell. In another it merely made the patient drowsy. In other instances it worked as well as it had on Frost.

Morton appeared to recognize that the trick lay in the method of administration. He settled on a funnel-like flask with one outlet which fed vapor from an ether-soaked sponge via a rubber tube. It worked. He determined to offer his preparation to the Massachusetts General Hospital.

There are many legends how ether came to the attention of John Collins Warren, the surgeon before whose class Wells failed, and who was to perform the first operation with ether. Morton himself said that physicians of the hospital, hearing of his tooth extractions with the mysterious painkiller, called on him and asked that he demonstrate it. Rice, Morton's paid biographer, relates that Morton determined to visit Warren at his home and lay the matter before him. The latter version seems more probable.

Morton, as should certainly be evident by now, was not well grounded academically or in experimentation. It is plain that less than a week elapsed between his operation on Eben H. Frost and his approach to John Collins Warren. He had had neither the time nor the equipment, nor, indeed, the faintest notion of any methodology for conducting further researches on the subject.

To what extent—it is a question one may well ask at this point—was Morton indebted to Wells? It is true that Morton visited Wells after the Boston disaster, and learned from him all he knew about nitrous oxide, its preparation and effects. That Wells put him on the anesthesia trail there is no gainsaying, and Morton was not justified in ever belittling Wells or the degree of his own indebtedness.

But in all fairness, did Morton extract the tooth of Eben H. Frost with nitrous oxide? Did not Morton use a wholly different agent? True it is that ether was suggested by Jackson—Morton never denied that. But Jackson recommended ether instead of nitrous oxide with the indulgence of a teacher giving a bright if slightly addled student enough rope. There is ample evidence, including Jackson's own statements, that he himself doubted its usefulness. The incredibly circular story of who should get the credit is amusing if one does not get lost in the mazes of conflicting evidence, most of it manufactured years after the events occurred.

A short time after Morton's interview with Warren, he received this note:

> Dear Sir:
>   I write at the request of Dr. J. C. Warren, to invite you to be present on Friday morning at 10 o'clock, at the hospital, to administer to a patient who is then to be operated upon, the preparation which you have invented to diminish the sensibility to pain.

It was dated October 14, 1846, and signed by C. F. Heywood, house surgeon to the Massachusetts General Hospital. Morton received the letter at the home of Augustus A. Gould, a Boston physician with whom he and his wife resided. The now-anxious Morton discussed the inhaler with Gould, who thought its chief disadvantage was that the patient breathed back his own expired air through the apparatus's sole outlet.

A sketch was given to N. B. Chamberlain, a Boston instrument maker, who agreed to take on the rush assignment. The morning of the operation the apparatus was not ready. Morton was in a fever of impatience, fearful lest Warren's operation proceed without him and the great opportunity be lost, and equally concerned that the improved inhaler be used.

At last the workman handed him the glass globe. Morton examined it hastily. It was fashioned with two openings, the one in relation to the other as would be the hands of a clock at five minutes to three. Morton nodded his satisfaction. He took it and ran. On the way to the hospital he picked up Eben H. Frost. If he failed, as Wells had, he wanted Frost to testify that in his own case, at least, the Morton preparation had been a success.

At the Massachusetts General Hospital the scene had already been set for some fifteen minutes. The seats above the surgical pit in the hospital's operating room were jammed with students and staff members. Among the doctors present were Gould, Henry J. Bigelow, C. F. Heywood, and S. D. Townsend. John Collins Warren, who was to perform the operation, had already delivered his clinical lecture. The patient, thin and pale Gilbert Abbot, a consumptive young man with a tumor at the angle of the jaw, waited resignedly. Warren stilled the whispering with a slight cough.

"As Dr. Morton has not arrived," he said dryly, "I presume he is otherwise engaged."

It was fortunate for Morton that he arrived when he did. He came puffing into the large domed chamber just as a great laugh greeted Warren's sally. Warren nodded his acquiescence to a brief delay while Morton retired to a room behind the seats of the amphitheater. Morton camouflaged the characteristic odor of ether with aromatic essences. He saturated his sponge, inserted it in the globe which he thereupon corked, and once again made his appearance.

Warren said, "Well, sir, your patient is ready."

Morton, a big hearty man with upswept mustaches and a predilection for fancy waistcoats, immediately gained Abbot's confidence. The patient was strapped to the red-plush operating chair, a customary precaution which the attending physicians saw no reason to discontinue. Morton pointed out Eben Frost to Abbot.

"There is a man who has breathed the preparation and can testify to its success."

Frost nodded from across the room that this was so.

"Are you afraid?" Morton asked Abbot.

This pale figure about whom so little is known was evidently something of a man. He would not admit fear before an audience of his fellows at a time like this. "No," Abbot replied. "I feel confident and will do precisely as you tell me."

Morton put the tube to his lips and told him very carefully to breathe in and out of the globe through his mouth. Abbot obeyed orders perfectly. At first his face flushed and his arms and legs moved spasmodically in the fashion that most of the students, familiar with the exhilarating effects of the vapor, knew and expected. But Morton held the glass globe in one hand and kept the tube at Abbot's mouth with the other for what must have seemed an interminable length of time to the witnesses, an interval far longer than had been dared or dreamed by any. Actually, it was only three to four minutes.

"Sir," said Morton, bowing in turn to Warren, "*your* patient is ready."

Warren seized the extruded veins of the tumor in one hand, and with the other made his first incision of the skin. Years of hearing that initial outcry under the knife did not prevent him from steeling himself unconsciously for the screams of anguish that usually attended his swift but coldly controlled movements. Above him, in the stalls where the students sat, many a hand must have clenched tightly, remembering the bedlam of previous operations.

But no sound issued from Abbot's mouth. Rapidly, but with the calm self-discipline for which he was noted, Warren continued his operation. When he insulated the veins, as this procedure was then called, the patient moved his legs a bit and uttered incoherent sounds. But it was evident to all that an extraordinary thing had transpired. The wound was closed, the patient's face washed of blood. Gradually he emerged from the effects of Morton's "preparation." Morton questioned him; Abbot had felt no pain; he remembered vaguely something blunt scratching his cheek.

Warren turned to his students and colleagues. Perhaps remembering their hisses and catcalls at Wells's demonstration in 1844, he employed the very word they had hurled at the Hartford dentist. "Gentlemen," said John Collins Warren in the midst of an impressive silence, "this is no humbug." Warren, the granite-faced surgeon with the biting wit, unbent completely. He later wrote:

> A new era has opened on the operating surgeon. His visitations on the most delicate parts are performed, not only without the agonizing screams he has been accustomed to hear, but sometimes in a state of perfect insensibility, and, occasionally, even with an expression of pleasure on the part of the patient.
>
> Who could have imagined that drawing a knife over the delicate skin of the face might produce a sensation of unmixed delight? That the turning and twisting of instruments in the most sensitive bladder might be accompanied by a delightful dream? That the contorting of anchylosed joints should coexist with a celestial vision?

If Ambroise Paré, and Louis, and Dessault, and Cheselden, and Hunter, and Cooper, could see what our eyes daily witness, how they would long to come among us, and perform their exploits once more.

And with what fresh vigor does the living surgeon, who is ready to resign his scalpel, grasp it, and wish again to go through his career under the new auspices.

As philanthropists we may well rejoice that we have had an agency, however slight, in conferring on poor suffering humanity so precious a gift.

Unrestrained and free as God's own sunshine, it has gone forth to cheer and gladden the earth; it will awaken the gratitude of the present, and all coming generations. The student, who from distant lands or in distant ages, may visit this spot, will view it with increased interest, as he remembers that here was first demonstrated one of the most glorious truths of science.

This was indeed the high point of Morton's career. From this time onward he was to plunge into a dizzy maelstrom of controversy, charges, and countercharges, even to lobbying in Congress for national gratitude in the form of financial grants. For Warren was wrong when he called this gift "unrestrained and free as God's own sunshine."

Morton not only sought to make money from his "invention" but the thought had obsessed him from the very first. He patented it and made a vigorous effort to sell it to the government for use on the Mexican front. Years later he was suing a charitable institution for infringing his rights.

But no honor attended the last days of Morton's life, for he met no less disagreeable an end than did Wells and Jackson. In July, 1868, he returned to New York from one of his countless trips to the nation's capital in a condition bordering on complete breakdown, brought on, it has been said, by his encounter of an article which favored Jackson's claim. Drs. Sayre and Yale were called to his New York residence on July 15. They pronounced him in critical condition, ordered in a trained nurse, prescribed leeches for his temples, cups for his spine, ice for his head.

But Morton refused to submit to treatment. Following the physicians' departure, he jumped into his buggy and headed for the Riverside Hotel, declaring he knew he would feel better if he could only get out of the hot city.

He drove furiously up Broadway and through Central Park. At the upper end of the park he leaped from his buggy, ran to the lake, and plunged his head into the water. Persuaded to get back into his rig, he drove a short distance, leaped out, hurdled a fence, and fell down unconscious. He was taken to St. Luke's Hospital where he died a few hours later.

A mere two years after the discovery of anesthesia became generally known, the American public was wearied to death of the controversy, which continues to this day. After a century Long, Wells, Jackson, and Morton still have their partisans. The controversy will never be settled, but the wisest verdict is still that of Oliver Wendell Holmes: "To e(i)ther."

Joseph Lister
Discovers Antisepsis

by Logan Clendening

It is a measure of the greatness of Louis Pasteur that his work on fermentation gave Joseph Lister the clue which led him to the discovery of antisepsis. It is an outstanding example, as well, of the interrelationship of all the sciences. Sickness (or fermentation) in wine and sickness (inflammation) in human flesh after operations could conceivably be the same, caused by the microbes in the air. Thus reasoned Lister, and in doing so made the discovery which is described in the selection that follows.

There were two steps in the development of the operating room as it exists today, with its masked and rubber-gloved figures, its sterilized instruments, and the "surgical cleanliness" which have become a part of the language. The first was antisepsis, the killing of germs present in the operating room. The second was asepsis, the prevention of their appearance by means of previous sterilization. To Lister goes the credit for developing the first of these methods. From it the second developed. It is with justification, therefore, that Lister has been called the greatest surgeon who ever lived.

On August 12, 1865, the professor of surgery at the University of Glasgow was sitting in his little office in the infirmary. Crossing his legs and ruefully gazing down at his foot as he kicked it up and down, he thought to himself that surgery was at a low ebb. The name of the professor of surgery was Joseph Lister, and he was comparatively young for so important a position—only thirty-eight. He had held the chair, though, in Glasgow for five years, having come thence from Edinburgh. He had married the daughter of the great Dr. Syme, professor of surgery at Edinburgh, and everyone agreed that it was probably his father-in-law's pull that had got him his place. He himself would never amount to much as a surgeon—so they said.

For he had queer ideas about a lot of things.

He was not satisfied with the condition surgery was in, for one thing. He did not seem to think so much of the great men who were so proud to be called surgeons.

It worried him when a case of compound fracture died in his wards. But everyone knew that more than half of your compound fractures died. What was the use of expecting anything better?

A compound fracture was what they called a break in the bone when the broken fragments of the bones cut themselves through the skin and protruded out of the wound. A simple fracture was one where the bones broke but the skin remained intact.

Young Mr. Lister knew quite well that if you splinted your simple fracture, the bones would knit, and in the course of time the patient would have as good an arm, or leg, or collarbone, as ever— or, at least, nearly as good.

But your compound fractures, they were the devil itself. The place where the bones stuck out of the skin would begin to get red, then a lot of pus would form, and the stinking stuff would drain from the wound forever. And the patient would get feverish and delirious, perhaps, and suffer tortures. Then, like as not, an erysipelas would set in, and abscesses higher up the leg or arm, as the case might be, would form, and finally in more than half the cases the patient would die.

Nothing like this happened to the simple fractures. Those

patients had no fever, and no abscesses, and no erysipelas. It was not because a *bone* was broken, then, so the professor reasoned.

It had got to be an obsession with Joseph Lister. He knew well enough about the nature of the processes behind the pus and the redness and the swelling. These were indications of inflammation. He had given lectures on inflammation. He had written a book on it, published in 1857. But inflammation alone did not kill. Inflammation was a sort of healing. This gangrene in compound fractures was different.

Other things puzzled him. He had looked up his statistics on amputations. Forty-five per cent of his cases had died. Yet he did things in the most approved fashion—just as the great Syme, his father-in-law, did them. But those amputations acted just like his compound fractures. There was redness, swelling, inflammation, pus, fever, and, finally, death.

He had talked about the thing a good deal with other surgeons. They smiled indulgently. They said it was inevitable. The pus they called "laudable pus." It was necessary in the healing process. The first thing nature did in order to start healing was to form laudable pus.

But Lister was not so sure. He remembered a phrase of Hippocrates—something about healing "by first intention." That is, healing without the formation of pus. Why did some wounds heal by first intention and why did some have to form "laudable pus"? Why did not his compound fractures heal by first intention?

He talked about these things with everyone he met. A young medical student in Edinburgh, named Batty Tuke, saw a case with Lister in 1854. It was a popliteal case. Lister took off the dressing and found the wound healed except where the ligature had been applied.

He said: "The main object of my life is to find out how to procure this result in all wounds. But why is it not healed around the ligature?"

Boylike, as he himself avers, Batty Tuke suggested: "The irritation of the silk."

"No," replied Lister, "not of, but *in* or *on*."

He often talked it over with his father-in-law, James Syme. Syme was a genial and approachable man. Progressive, too! He had adopted the new American method of using ether to put his patients to sleep when they were operated upon. He and Nikolai Ivanovich Pirogoff, the Russian, were among the few European surgeons to do it fifteen years before, when Lister was a dresser at Edinburgh. But Syme was a man of few words, and a Scotsman at that—he did not know, he did not know, and that was all there was to it. Joseph Lister got no help from him in this puzzle.

Then Professor Thomas Anderson, the chemist at Glasgow, gave him a hint—the first hint he had about his problem.

"See here, son," said Anderson to him one day in that same year of 1865, "have you read any of these papers of this crazy Frenchman—a chap named Pasteur?"

Lister had not.

"Come over to my chamber and I'll give you a copy," said Anderson. "I think they're somewhat in your line."

Anderson knew Lister was interested in inflammation, and, for all anybody knew, inflammation might be a form of fermentation.

The papers by Pasteur were very queer—very queer indeed. The young professor was puzzled over many of them. This Pasteur was not a medical doctor at all; he was a chemist, like Professor Anderson. One of his papers had to do with changing one kind of tartaric acid into another kind. It was not easy for a professor of surgery to understand. But then there was an idea—some surgeons claimed that inflammation was due to a change in the nature of the fluids in the tissues. If chemical changes could occur in minerals, why not in human tissues? Well, there a person was.

Then another of these papers showed that wine fermented from something that dropped into the grape juice from the air.

The air—here was an idea. The young professor of surgery began to get excited. *The air*. That was the difference between the simple fracture and the compound fracture. Air got into the compound fracture. Now, if there was something in the air that caused these intensive inflammations and the laudable pus to form, it might explain things.

The professor began to think. What about his amputations—why did so many of them go wrong? Well, the air got to the exposed bone and flesh, too, didn't it?

He and Professor Anderson talked all night about these questions. Then he talked to his dressers about it. Many facts fitted into the theory.

For instance, there were some places in the body no surgeon dared penetrate. Even ten years later Sir John Erickson was to say that operative surgery had reached its finality, and that there were three regions into which the surgeon could never enter with impunity—the brain, the chest, and the abdomen.

Not only that, but joint surfaces. Larrey, the surgeon of the Napoleonic armies, did thousands of amputations at the hip. But only three ever lived.

Yet sometimes the thing was done. There was an account in Cheselden's Surgery of a wound in the abdomen and the patient didn't die.

Then there was Spencer Wells in London. He took out ovaries successfully—had been doing it since 1858. When you remove an ovary, you have to go into the abdomen. You have to enter the peritoneum.

And McDowell, the American! The young professor had heard about McDowell. McDowell had taken out an ovarian cyst in 1809 and had performed the same operation several times thereafter.

What was the secret? Why did some people have no trouble when they let the air into a wound, and others have trouble?

Perhaps the air was different at different times. Perhaps some air had a fermenting principle in it and some did not. The professor was strongly inclined to think that was it.

But what to do about it? That was quite as much of a puzzle as any other aspect of the case. You can't exclude air. It is everywhere. What to do?

Was it possible to change the air in some way and kill off the fermenting or inflammatory principle in it?

Professor Lister bothered everyone with his doubts and speculations.

At last one day a visiting surgeon from Carlisle said:

"See here, Lister, you know we have had an experience with the sewerage at Carlisle which I believe would interest you."

"What was that?" asked Lister.

"Well, since you think decomposition and gangrene and all these stinks that you have to keep the windows of your wards open to avoid, here in Glasgow, come from some fermenting substances or germs, or something of that kind, you want a way to kill them, don't you?"

"Yes, yes," said Lister eagerly.

"Well, in Carlisle we had a very stinking sewerage system. There were privies that smelled to high heaven. But you know what we did?—we put carbolic acid in the sewers—and, by gad, sir, the smell has disappeared from Carlisle."

"Carbolic acid—phenol, eh?" Lister asked.

"Ay—phenol. Now, of course, I don't know whether the smell disappeared because the septic particles were killed or not, but I do know the sewers and privies did not smell of carbolic very strong."

"What did they smell of?"

"They didn't smell much of anything," replied his colleague. "And there was another thing," he continued; "we had a lot of trouble with a disease of cattle feeding on pastures which were irrigated with the sewage—one of those entozoan disorders of some sort or other. Do you know, sir, we've had none of that since we used the phenol?"

This conversation made a great impression on Lister. He decided to paint a compound fracture with carbolic acid.

He did so in March, 1865.

Disappointment and confusion. The man died, in spite of the treatment—died just as all the others with compound fractures died.

But still he pondered the matter.

On August 12, 1865, his dresser, Hector Cameron, knocked on the door and came in.

"There's a compound fracture of the tibia just been admitted tae the ward, chief," he announced.

"A compound fracture, eh?" responded Lister. "Well, get me some carbolic acid. I am going to paint it with that."

"I hope ye have better luck wi' it than ye did wi' the puir lad ye tried it on a bit back," said the assistant.

"I hope so, too, Hector," answered his chief grimly.

So, with a ring of incredulous faces about him, he painted the edges of the wound and the protruding splinters of bone with the carbolic. Then he dressed the leg carefully.

"See here," he said suddenly. "Sister, I want the cleanest towel you have in the house to dress that wound with. And mind that you put it in a pan and boil it first."

In those days hospital dressings were obtained by asking house-wives to send bundles of their old linen. Nothing was done to them —they were not even washed before they were put on wounds.

We may be sure Dr. Lister watched his patient with the compound fracture very carefully. He changed the dressings next day and again swabbed the open surface with the carbolic.

He wrote his father, with whom he kept up a regular correspondence, as a dutiful son should. His father, Joseph Jackson

Lister, was a very great man himself. With Wollaston he had perfected the compound microscope much as we now have it. He was a man of science—indeed, a Fellow of the Royal Society. So his son felt free to discuss with the greatest freedom matters of scientific interest with his father.

"There is one of my cases at the Infirmary which I am sure will interest thee," wrote this Quaker son to his Quaker father. "It is one of compound fracture of the leg: with a wound of considerable size and accompanied by great bruising and a great effusion of blood. . . . Though hardly expecting success, I tried the application of carbolic acid to the wound to prevent decomposition of the blood, and so avoid the fearful mischief of suppuration throughout the limb. Well, it is now eight days since the accident, and the patient has been going on exactly as if there were no external wound, that is, as if the fracture were a simple one. His appetite, sleep, etc., are good and the limb daily diminishing in size, while there is no appearance whatever of any matter forming."

Finally the patient was discharged from the infirmary with a good leg and a record of recovery so uneventful as to be a marvel to the whole city.

In the meantime Lister had been trying the procedure on other cases. One was a boy whose arm had been mangled in a machine at a fair. "Without the assistance of the antiseptic treatment," as he told the section on surgery of the British Medical Association, two years later, "I should certainly have thought of nothing else but amputation at the shoulder joint."

"My dear Father," he writes under the date of June 11, 1866, "I have really little or nothing to write about this week." Nothing much to write about! Only one of the ten most important things that have ever happened to the human race! "I have a continued good report to give of the compound fracture, which is, indeed, now no longer a case of uncertainty."

Whatever else Joseph Lister may have been, you cannot get into the same atmosphere with him without a feeling of peace and love of truth.

He got several new ideas. Instead of washing his hands after a surgical operation, as most of his colleagues did, he washed them before. Instead of wearing a dirty old coat, with dried blood and pus on it, to operate in, he wore a clean linen apron. Instead of having his thread and needle stuck in his lapel, he invented a way to sterilize ligatures.

And the air which he thought was so important a source of infection—he had that sprayed with carbolic acid and water from a kind of donkey engine.

His results were unbelievable. Indeed, they were unbelieved. "Hospital gangrene" almost disappeared from the Glasgow infirmary. "Hospital gangrene" was the frightful infection that got into every open wound in the hospitals of that day. The windows of the ward had to be kept wide open, the stench of the gangrene was so terrible. It was even seriously debated whether or not to close and burn every hospital in England, the scandal of the matter was so great.

On March 16, 1867, he reported his results in an article in the *Lancet*, the great English weekly journal of the medical sciences. On August 9 of that year he read his paper "On the Antiseptic Principle of the Practice of Surgery" to the British Medical Association meeting at Dublin. It was probably the most important address ever made before a group of surgeons.

And what did the surgeons do? Most of them laughed. Most of them winked. Some got angry. Lister was a little balmy. Or just a plain liar.

But others believed him. Some went to Glasgow to see his results and came away convinced. Donkey engines spraying the air with carbolic acid were common things in operating rooms then.

The air of surgery, indeed, from 1867 to 1885 was full of carbolic acid and controversy.

Here was young Lawson Tait, for instance. He had settled in Birmingham. He, like Lister, had been an Edinburgh man and had studied under Syme. He left Edinburgh with one conclusion determined in his mind—"that I would never deliberately open an abdomen."

He had seen it done and had seen that the results were too awful. "The results [of ovariotomy]," he wrote, "I have seen in Edinburgh were truly awful—some thirty cases and not a recovery."

Long afterward he penned a sketch of the surgical conditions of those days:

"Personally, Syme was the personification of the best type of gentleman, always perfectly dressed in his old-fashioned way and clean as a new pin. From his boots to the top of his head no one ever saw dirt, disorder, or the appearance of hurry. He was always washing his hands—I think I may say he washed them every time he touched a patient.

"Through the folding doors what a difference. Everywhere hurry and untidiness, and no mark of what I praised in Syme. There was a good deal of dandiness, but much dirt. . . . The wards stank. The operating table was of wood and of fabulous age. . . . The only correct garb of the surgeon was a frock coat (the oldest and shabbiest in his wardrobe) which was kept in the surgeon's room and never renewed or cleaned during his twenty years of operating work. . . . The surgeons came direct from the dissecting room to operate. . . . Ligatures were used, which had been already soiled by handling with bloodstained fingers, to bind up wounds in a second case. And at Edinburgh these ligatures were always worn ostentatiously by the house surgeon, like a badge of knighthood, in the buttonhole of a coat, which often rivaled that of his chief for dirt."

No wonder Mr. Tait decided never deliberately to open an abdomen.

But he changed his mind. He was a good man with patients and he got a large practice. There was an itch in him to cut. He knew of Spencer Wells in London. In 1858 Wells had opened an abdomen and taken out an ovary, and the patient lived. He had done it frequently since.

In May, 1868, Tait saw Mrs. "Aitch" in consultation. He found she had a large floating tumor of the ovary, and, abandoning his former objections, he opened the abdomen and found that the tumor was cancerous and not removable. The patient died in seven weeks, but she had no peritonitis, which was the usual cause of death in ovariotomy. She died of her disease, not of the operation.

The fact that he could open an abdomen without causing peritonitis caused him to attack the antiseptic principle of Lister with great vigor, as he did in a paper called "Cases Treated Antiseptically on Lister's Method" in the *Lancet* for January 14, 1871. "My opinion of the antiseptic method is that its merits have been greatly overrated." Such good results as were reported he thought were owing more to cleanliness than to the exclusion of air.

In October, 1871, he saw in consultation a woman, aged forty-two, who had suffered for years from an agonizing pain in the pelvis in the region of the left ovary. "After careful thought," he wrote, "I ventured to suggest to my colleague the removal of the ovary would probably cure her. I recognized the gravity of the proposal for I had no fear that her suffering would kill her, but," he explained, he felt he could relieve the dreadful agony she constantly suffered. "The patient and her friends arrived at the same conclusions." And on February 11, 1872, he opened the abdomen and removed the ovary, which was "as large as a pigeon's egg and full of thick grumous matter," which he at first thought was a dermoid cyst, but which he afterward concluded was a chronic abscess. "The patient made a speedy and complete recovery, and has remained since completely free from pain in the pelvis."

So the women came flocking to Birmingham, and Lawson Tait operated on them without using Lister's donkey engine.

But he used cleanliness. He washed his hands thoroughly before an operation. So did all his nurses and assistants. He wore a sort of apron, or gown. All the sponges were soaked in muriatic acid and rinsed in hot water before use. The instruments were washed and soaked in hot water.

Gradually the atmosphere cleared. In 1878 Robert Koch showed the cause of wound infection to be the germs called staphylococci and streptococci. Lister gradually gave up his idea that the air contained the substances which caused hospital gangrene. It began to be the custom to boil the instruments and sponges to be used in an operation and thus kill the germs responsible for infection. Ligatures, to which Lister devoted much time, were almost universally prepared, as he advocated, by soaking in carbolic acid. But the donkey engine and the carbolic spray had disappeared almost completely by 1890.

And in that period between 1867 and 1890 all surgery had undergone a change. Hospital gangrene, erysipelas, septicemia, running wounds, stinking wards—all disappeared. In 1881 Christian Albert Billroth, the great Viennese surgeon, opened the way for operations on all organs by removing the stomach for cancer, and later by doing operations on the intestines. Operations for removal of the womb, of the appendix, of gallstones, etc., soon followed. If one were to attempt to decide who did which of these first one would get into enough trouble to satisfy any stickler for historical accuracy.

And in the meantime, too, all the rancor died away and Joseph Lister lived in the sunset period of his life in a sort of halo of glory shed over him by the whole world of surgery and medicine and, indeed, science.

On December 27, 1892, the Republic of France, in the person of its president and deputies, met at the Sorbonne to do honor to

Louis Pasteur on his seventieth birthday. The old gentleman was weak and ill and broken. He entered the hall leaning on the arm of President Carnot, and as he did so, Lister, who was present as the representative of the Royal Society of London and the Royal Society of Edinburgh, in a gesture of infinite grace and majesty, rose and with outstretched arms came forward, his eyes brimming with tears of devotion and respect, and embraced his comrade. For a moment these two among the greatest of the sons of men stood together, a symbol of the common brotherhood of science.

Field Hospital—World War I

Belleau Wood and Château-Thierry
by Frederick A. Pottle

Battlefields have always been prime training grounds for surgeons, giving them lifetimes of experience within days or weeks. In World War I, Frederick A. Pottle enlisted as what would now be called a "medic," and served near the front lines of some of the greatest battles of that war. In reading his graphic eyewitness account of how the wounded were cared for it is interesting to note how antiquated some surgical techniques have become in the short period since 1917. In later years the author became a professor of English at Yale and editor of the recently discovered Boswell papers.

On the afternoon of June 7, 1918, we arrived in the yards at Le Bourget, in the northern suburbs of Paris, and lay there several hours. From where we lay the Eiffel Tower was clearly visible above the skyline of the great city. Numberless planes were patrolling the sky, in expectation of the nightly air raid. We were too excited to sleep, and sat up to watch the German planes come over, but, for a wonder, none appeared that night. Sometime about midnight we left the yards, and ran north to St. Mard, a little station halfway between Paris and Château-Thierry. On the morning of Saturday, June 8, we marched out of St. Mard down a long, straight, shaded road into the streets of an old town. . . . We find a great pile of venerable buildings, evidently some sort of school. Over the grand old white gateway floats an American flag. Ambulances are driving in, feverishly unloading their freight of long brown litters heavy with prostrate forms. We are at the old Collège de Juilly, Seine-et-Marne, and the great battle of Belleau Wood is on.

No quarters have as yet been prepared for us, and it is imperative that we waste no time hunting for any. We drop our packs on the beautiful green lawn, where a line of our great brown ward tents is later to stand, and sit down on the grass to snatch a hasty dinner. Within thirty minutes of our arrival we are all at work. We are told off into details, pretty much at random, and assigned for duty in the receiving ward, the operating rooms, the surgical wards, to dig graves and bury the dead; in short, to perform all the multifarious tasks of a large evacuation hospital jammed with wounded.

Let us follow some of these men as they get their first impressions of war surgery. Our first man is assigned to Ward D. Ward D, he finds, is a detached building in the corner of the lawn. He goes up the steps, crosses a narrow entry, and looks in. What a strange room—large and bare, with the farther end elevated like a stage. It *is* a stage. The place was evidently the theater of the school. Now it is filled with cots; not only the floor, but even the stage, from which all the scenery has been stripped. The cots are lined up as thick as they will go, with only the narrowest alleys for walking between, and every cot has a wounded man on it.

It is in the only-too-obvious evidence of terrible wounds that one realizes that this is a war hospital. Here lies a fair-haired boy of eighteen or so, his eyes closed, his neck and shoulder exposed to show a great bulky wad of bandage over the stump of an arm amputated near the shoulder. Here is an older man, haggard, unshaven, and ugly, his knees drawn up over his distended stomach, a look of peculiar and characteristic agony on his face. He has a severe wound of the abdomen, and has not much longer to suffer. He struggles to repress the frequent coughing fits that tear him with pain. He is continually calling out something in a language that is not English. There are some French wounded here, but the card tied to the head of his cot shows that he is an American, an immigrant who enlisted before he had mastered the language of his adopted country. There is a black-haired youngster who has lost his leg above the knee. The majority of the others have suffered less severely, but there is not a man here who has not escaped death scores of times in the last week by the narrowest of margins. Some of them are babbling in delirium, some shouting and cursing as they fight their way out of the ether dream in which they are re-enacting the horror of the trenches, some in their right minds, gaily talking and joking, but the most lie in a half-waking stupor, the inevitable reaction to days of hunger, fatigue, the nervous strain of incessant deadly peril, and, finally, the shock of severe wounds, ether, and surgical operations. They have been for days without food; they have lain for hours in shallow holes with shells bursting every moment within inches of them and inflicting sudden and awful death among their comrades; their ears have been deafened with noise which in itself would produce prostration; they have walked unprotected straight into the murderous hail of machine-gun bullets; they have fought hand to hand with bayonets, in duels where the only possible outcome was either victory or death. These are the wounded marines from Belleau Wood. One's first shock of surprise comes from finding them so young. Most of these wounded men are boys of the age of college freshmen or a little older, boys of magnificent physique, but preserving still in contour of limb and downy cheek the grace of boyhood. The beauty of their faces is only enhanced by suffering. They have not yet wasted away with weeks of torture. Their faces are smooth and round, though drained of all color, and their pallor makes their eyes stand out with extraordinary clearness. They are touchingly brave, self-sacrificing, grateful.

Or perhaps our man was sent instead to Ward E, the great room beneath the chapel, which is on the second floor under the statue of the Virgin and Child. In the little alcove on the right lies a solitary patient, a French aviator who was burned in the crash of his plane. His body is not much marked, but his face is so charred that none of the features are distinguishable, and his hands are burned to mere stumps. Thin strips of gauze wet with some antiseptic solution cover his face, but not so completely that one cannot see the horror of his condition. His sense of hearing is acute, and as anyone comes up to his bed he begins to murmur in a faint, hoarse whisper, the hole where his lips should be puffing up the edges of the gauze. He is asking in French for something. It sounds like "morphine." Is it morphine? *"Non! non!"* says the whisper passionately, *"pas morphine!"* We cannot make him out, and try to tell him that we will call one of the French nuns.

Other men have gone to work in the operating rooms. Ward A is on the floor above. At the end of the ward is a little anteroom to the operating room. Evacuation Eight has not yet organized its receiving service so efficiently as it will later, when the men will come up to the operating room already undressed and with their wounds prepared for operation. The floor here is covered with litters on which lie the men just as they came from the ambulances, fully clothed with boots, puttees, breeches, shirt, and blouse, often with their steel helmets on their breasts and their gas masks beside them. Into one of the buttonholes of the blouse or shirt is tied a linen tag giving the man's name, his serial number and company, the treatment which he has thus far received, and from what medical unit. On their foreheads, standing out with startling distinctness on the white skin, are letters in iodine; always "T," and sometimes "M." These indicate the administration of morphine and antitetanic serum.

The first thing to do is to get their clothes off. Puttees come off first, then muddy shoes, tattered and bloody breeches, blouse, shirt, underwear. Much of it must be cut off to avoid bending wounded arms and legs. In spite of their pain the men make no outcry and do their best to help us. We put hospital shirts or pajamas on them, wrap them in blankets, and they are ready for the operating room. The stretcher-bearers come out with a stretcher on which lies a wounded man just off the table, still deep under the ether, his face wet with perspiration, eyes closed, his breathing deep and heavy. Next! We pick up the stretcher nearest the door and carry it into the operating room.

There are three tables. Around two busy and silent groups of white-gowned figures are bending over their work. The third is empty, and an attendant with a wet cloth is wiping off the blood that covers the lower portion in a shallow pool. We transfer our patient to the damp table, and at the same time get a mental picture of the room. It is not large, perhaps fifteen feet square, and very white and dazzling. The door is in one corner, and there are two high windows in the wall opposite. Against the wall on the left as you enter is a small oil cookstove, on which steams a highly polished copper tank for sterilizing the instruments. Against the wall facing you, between the windows, is a stout wooden table covered with a sheet, on which the sterilized instruments are laid out in shining rows, like silver in the drawers of a sideboard. Against the wall to the right are the lavatories where the surgeons scrub up. The three operating tables, white enameled and covered with thin, oilcloth-covered mats, are lined up in the middle of the room, their heads toward the entrance, the feet toward the table with the sterilized instruments.

But we must get to work on our wounded man. The surgeons who have just finished with one man have stripped off their blood-stained gowns and gloves and are scrubbing their hands. Under their direction we fold back the blanket which covers the wounded man so as to expose the wound, let us say on the thigh. We fold another blanket to cover his feet and legs to the knee, and slip two stout straps around him, one just above the knees and one around the chest. The wound is still covered with the pack and bandages applied at the first-aid station or field hospital. We cut the bandage and expose it—a jagged aperture made by shrapnel, perhaps two inches long. With an ordinary razor we shave a considerable area around the wound. The surgeon has now finished scrubbing his hands. The nurse at the supply table opens for him a square parcel that contains a sterilized gown wrapped in a piece of muslin. He shakes it out gingerly by the neckband, careful not to touch the front. The attendant as gingerly ties the strings behind. The surgeon now rinses his hands with alcohol, and, when they have dried, pulls on a pair of rubber gloves, picking them up by their long, turned-back wrists, which, when the fingers are worked on, he turns up over the sleeves of his gown. His hands and the whole front of his body now present a perfectly sterilized surface, which nothing unsterilized has touched, and which must touch nothing unsterilized except the wound itself.

Meanwhile the anesthetist has been busy. She sits on a stool at the head of the table, at such a height that her elbows rest easily upon it on either side of the patient's head. Beside her is a little stand with her cans of ether, gauze, vaseline, a shallow basin shaped like a kidney, and clips for pulling forward the man's tongue if he should choke. The man has not cried out or in any way expressed his fear, but his eyes show that he is terrified by the array of glistening instruments, the solemn white figures—worst of all, by the rapid play of scalpel and scissors which he can see by turning his head toward the tables on either side. His eyes in mute appeal seek those of the one familiar figure in the room, that of the enlisted man at his side. "Don't be frightened," I say, "the ether won't bother you at all, and it will all be over in a minute." (God forgive me, I have never taken ether in my life.)

"Will you just take my hand, buddy," says the wounded man a trifle huskily, "I don't know much about this, and I'm afraid I may fight when the ether gets bad."

"Sure!" I reply, "that's what I'm here for."

The nurse smears a little vaseline around his eyes, and, holding the mask a few inches above his face, begins to pour the ether on it. "Breathe deep," she says, "and don't fight it." The mask comes lower, finally rests on his face, and a piece of gauze is wrapped around the edges to keep in the fumes. She pours on the ether faster. The man groans and struggles; he throws both his arms wide and tries to sit up. We have to tighten the straps and hold down his arms. Now he is limp, the moaning faint and dying away. The surgeon takes a long-handled clip which holds a swab, dips it in iodine, and paints a large area around the wound.

One nurse stands all the time by the supply table, serving the surgeons at all three operating tables. She hands him four sterilized towels, which he lays around the wound, leaving exposed only a small rectangular patch of darkly stained skin with the wound in the center. How will he fasten his towels on? A little stand has been pushed up beside the foot of the table. The nurse covers it with a towel, and begins to lay out instruments on it. The surgeon picks up one that looks a little like a pair of manicure scissors, but, instead of cutting blades, it has two little sharp curved points that meet like a pair of pincers. With these he picks up the towels at the point where two of them overlap, and clips them together, pushing the points of the instrument down so that they meet in the skin underneath. The instrument has a catch which will hold it tightly shut until it is released. He puts on three more, one at each corner of the exposed patch. The uninitiated assistant gasps and flinches at this apparently cold-blooded process, and then derides his tenderness as he thinks how trivial these pinpricks are in comparison with what is to come. The team is now ready: the chief, or operating, surgeon, his assistant (always a surgeon also, and an officer), and a nurse, who stands beside the little stand of instruments, ready to hand what is wanted. (This is in addition to the nurse at the large supply table of sterilized instruments.) These are all "scrubbed up," that is, provided with an elaborate surgical asepsis of sterilized gowns and gloves. The anesthetist and two enlisted men, who are not "scrubbed up," must look out for manipulating the patient, getting him on and off the table, bandaging, and bringing unsterilized equipment.

The surgeon takes a scalpel (a little knife with a rigid blade no larger than a penknife), which he holds like a pen, and with firm, even pressure draws an incision on each side of the wound and considerably longer. The skin springs apart, showing the yellowish fatty layer beneath, and exposing the red of the muscle. This wound was made by a fragment of high-explosive shell, which is still deeply embedded in the flesh. It has been located by the X-ray surgeon, who has made two marks with silver nitrate on the thigh, one on the top and one on the side. The foreign body lies at the point where perpendicular bisectors from those marks would intersect. The surgeon goes after it with scalpel and scissors, excising all the damaged tissue with what looks like reckless abandon. As he cuts into the muscle the blood spurts up like juice in a berry pie. The assistant mops it up with a gauze sponge, discovers the point where the blood vessel is severed, and the surgeon clips it with a hemostat, another variety of pincers with handles like manicure scissors. This is for small blood vessels; larger ones must be tied off at once. By the end of the operation the wound is full of these dangling hemostats. The surgeon probes with his finger between the muscle bundles for the shrapnel, and finally dislodges it, a jagged chunk of metal an inch square each way, with a great wad of cloth from the man's breeches clinging to it. He goes on, painstakingly removing every particle of clotted blood and tissue that has been damaged by the missile or resulting infection. Now, with the help of his assistant, he ties off the blood vessels still held by hemostats. During all this the enlisted assistants at his direction have been turning the patient on the table, elevating or flexing the leg, or with a flashlight throwing light into some peculiarly inaccessible part of the wound.

The operation is finished. What was a small jagged wound is now a gaping hole six inches long, two or three wide at the top, and perhaps four deep, perhaps extending through the entire thigh. The nurse places on the stand a bundle of little red rubber tubes, open at one end, the closed end punched full of holes. The surgeon pushes these into the wound, leaving the open ends out, inserting the closed ends into every crevice. He fills the cavity with gauze plentifully soaked with a solution smelling of chlorine, lays gauze strips soaked with yellow vaseline along the edges of the wound, and places a large absorbent pad over the orifice. His work is done. We bind on the pad with yards of bandage, roll the inert body onto a stretcher, and hurry it away to a ward. As he scrubs for the next case, the surgeon dictates to one of us a description of the case and the surgical treatment he has given it. All this may have taken half an hour; possibly an hour or more. We go on with the work, in twelve-hour shifts, night and day, as long as the supply of wounded holds out.

Remember that few of these enlisted men have ever been in an operating room before in their lives, and that as few of these surgeons have had actual previous experience in the technique of war surgery. Yet in that first afternoon they are called upon to perform the most dreadful as well as the most delicate operations. One could not plead inexperience as an excuse for delay. Amputations high in the thigh or upper arm, operations of the chest where the ribs must be sprung apart with retractors, and looking in with incredulous amazement we see the heart throbbing bare; wounds of the head and brain, wounds of the abdomen—in one day we performed more major operations than some civilian operating rooms see in six months. We work on without pause, undressing men, carrying them in, carrying them out, carrying them to X ray, carrying them to the wards. It is amazing how we form friendships in those few moments before the man goes onto the table. Late this evening, when we have gone off duty after twelve hours of such work, we shall stumble around to the wards to see how some of these boys are now, to wash their hands and faces, to sit quietly and talk with them. But we cannot sit long, for there is so much to be done in a ward, and wounded men naturally do not understand that you are not the regular ward orderly.

The ambulances drive in unceasingly through the archway and unload their wounded. The ambulances are muddy, and frequently splashed with holes from the fragments of shells that have burst just beside them. The drivers are weary, but they hurry to unload their freight and hurry off again—a long, brown, almost unbroken line of ambulances filling the road from Château-Thierry to Juilly.

Every night we evacuate. Another long, brown, unbroken line of ambulances pulls out of the hospital, not empty but filled with our wounded men who have undergone operation, bound for Paris. The ambulances pull up before the wards, the nurse indicates which men are to go, the orderlies and litter men transfer them gently to litters, lift and stow them away in the ambulances, call out a word of farewell, and they are off from Evacuation Eight forever.

One large detail has been at work all day on the grimmest task of all, that of digging graves and burying the dead. The grave detail dig the graves laboriously out of the stiff soil of a glorious field of wheat full of scarlet poppies, under a blazing sun—regulation graves, three feet wide, six feet and a half long, and six feet deep, and hastily lay in them the bodies of the dead. Later we had a burial party every afternoon about five. There would be five or six bodies, for which we then provided the luxury of unpainted wooden boxes. We piled them into a high two-wheeled French cart, drawn by a great patient work horse, and spread out an

American flag over the ends of the boxes. The little procession started from the Cours d'Honneur, at the head the little crucifer from the parish church, then our YMCA chaplain in plain khaki uniform, walking side by side with the village curé in his biretta, cassock, surplice, and stole. At the cemetery we unloaded the coffins and lowered them down into the graves, jumping impatiently on the tops of the boxes if they happened to stick in the narrow space, and then stood uncovered, leaning on our spades, as the curé in his clear, sonorous voice read the grand Latin of the Roman burial service over Catholic and Protestant, Jew and gentile, and our chaplain followed with the familiar English words. One sprinkled with holy water, the other cast in a handful of earth. The bugler, facing the west and the golden lightning of the sunken sun, blew the long, tender notes of taps, while far overhead an unseen lark poured forth its shrill delight.

A Surgeon's Domain

by Bertram M. Bernheim

A steady hand and a mind that reacts quickly and calmly in
emergencies are two of the requirements for young men
who want to become surgeons. But other equipment is
equally important, as Dr. Bernheim points out in this de-
lightful story of how he became a member of the craft and
how he trains others in its mysteries.

Surgeons are among the least expendable of men. Few people
realize it, but it is so. It takes long years of constant application to
make them: in the very nature of things, there are no child prodi-
gies among them as there are in music, literature, mathematics, hog
calling, and a host of other careers. In times of stress, by intensive
training you can turn out bucketfuls of aviators and military men
and sea captains—perhaps not the best, but men of usefulness (and
this is not said in disparagement)—but not surgeons. You can't
make good physicians, either; but even they can be had faster than
surgeons. The art of operating has to be hand taught and it has to
be individual; none of the mass-production, assembly-line methods
will do, with classes all through the day and far into the night.
Each man must actually use the knife himself; he must be brought
to it carefully, nursed along and guided; he will have to do
hundreds of operations—yes, and make mistakes—before he's any
good, and that takes time and patience and understanding. It costs
something, too, and I don't mean money! Maybe the succeeding
pages will show you how it's done.

I was months getting over my first experience; the classmate who was responsible for it was affected for life. This thin, reddish-haired, slow-spoken, humorous southerner who said surgery was in his very bones asked me to take the usual journey to the operating room with him. We had met only a few days before but it was not that which deterred me. I was afraid. The dissecting rooms were bad enough—in fact, almost more than I could bear —and the idea of seeing an operation on a living person floored me.

"Time enough when the third year comes," I said. "What's the hurry?"

"Ah'm a-gonna be a surgeon," he replied in his southern drawl, "an' Ah cain't wait to see what it's like. Ain't you gonna be a surgeon?"

"I don't know what I'm going to be right now, but if surgery's anything like dissecting and if the smell in operating rooms is as bad as this is in here, that's what I ain't a-gonna be!" As a gentleman from Kentucky, I liked to lapse into the lingo myself.

Roy laughed and said, "Come on! Ah found the way."

"No," I replied, and was adamant—for four days. Then I fell. The scoundrel kept telling me what the other fellows had seen, how wonderful it all was, how they would gather in groups to talk about "the big, bull-necked guy" who stood up to the table and cut patient after patient without batting an eyelid—Finney was his name—until the lure was too great and one hot morning the two of us stumbled through devious corridors and up dark stairways to reach the very topmost benches. It was an old wooden semicircular amphitheater of the type that now is almost obsolete, and the air was close and heavy with a sickening kind of sweetish odor that the other boys said was ether. It didn't make me exactly sick but I was nervous and wished I'd never come.

Soon a stocky, broad-shouldered, handsome man—they didn't wear face masks then—came in and began to slip on gown and gloves. They said he was the "Finney guy." A minute later they wheeled in a man who was being given ether by the old-fashioned method (a cone into which the anesthetic was poured or dropped). Before you could say Jack Robinson two other husky fellows came out of nowhere—orderlies, they called them—and lifted the patient from stretcher to table. They did everything nonchalantly and none too tenderly to my way of thinking, but no one seemed to mind, and who was I to complain?

The surgeon began to talk in a loud, firm voice but I couldn't understand most of the words he used. The boys said he was giving the history. Not Roy but the other boys, of whom there were several. Roy was quiet and, to my eye, looked paler than usual. The "Finney guy" talked awfully long, it seemed to me, and even when another doctor and a nurse had spread sheets and towels over the patient and stood there doing nothing, he was still talking. The man, I guessed, had a lot wrong with him. I noticed that the doctor and nurse had left both groins exposed. I don't remember what was in my mind but I was wholly unprepared for what happened next.

While he was still talking, Finney who, they all said, was such a great surgeon* stepped up to the operating table, held out his gloved right hand, had the flat handle of a glistening knife slapped into it, and forthwith made a long, straight cut in the right groin and immediately went down deep. Blood flowed, assistants hurriedly began putting on a lot of instruments the boys said were clamps to stop it. Finney never stopped talking or cutting, and man, it was a sight. My stomach turned over and Roy's face turned green. But Finney, not satisfied with the damage he'd already done, turned to the man's left groin and laid that wide open. The boys said he took out the glands because the man had a cancer, but Roy and I didn't see that part of it. With one accord we rushed

---

* John M. T. Finney—later one of America's foremost surgeons but even then well on his way. In World War I he became chief consulting surgeon of the A.E.F., having gone to France as chief of the Hopkins Unit from which he was very early detached.

out and down the steps for the fresh, cool air and Roy gave up his breakfast on reaching the sidewalk. I just sat on the curbstone, holding my head. When we both came to, Roy said, "Ah'm cured. No surgery for me. How 'bout you?"

"I don't know about surgery, Roy, but if you have any more brilliant ideas of visiting other parts of this hospital please keep them to yourself!"

After that I didn't go near an operation for two years—not until the third year came and it was required. Roy didn't, either, true to his word. In after years he went into pathology where he made quite a name for himself.

It took a war really to get me started in surgery, but since that didn't happen until 1917—nine years after I returned to Baltimore —it will be clear what a struggle I'd been having. Fortune hadn't exactly overlooked me during these years but she hadn't sent me in the direction I wanted to go. In the Hopkins laboratories I had the good fortune to devise a little tube which launched me in the new and fascinating field of blood transfusion; but the surgery connected with it was insignificant for practical purposes. To compensate I formed the habit of attending Dr. Finney's operative clinic each Thursday at the Union Protestant Infirmary, where an incident occurred that was as unusual as it was exciting.

It was a blustery, chilly, overcast morning, and as usual a big gallery was on hand. I was somewhat on edge because a femoral aneurism was on the list of cases to be done and the great man had instructed me to prepare and have ready for use one of Halsted's recently devised instruments for applying a constricting aluminum band. Dr. Halsted, renowned professor at the Hopkins though he was, worked alongside his humblest assistants in the laboratory and that is how I had come to see and become familiar with the new apparatus. I had even tried it on a dog, but never on a human being. Dr. Finney hadn't, either; but it was simplicity itself, and if the thing was prepared, there would be no difficulty.

Two or three other operations preceded the aneurism (saccular dilatation of a blood vessel), but finally Dr. Finney came to it and everything was going well when suddenly the operating-room supervisor hurried in, tapped the doctor lightly on the shoulder, whispered something in his ear, and presto! the whole picture changed. He stopped operating and stood there is if he were stunned, knife poised in the air. Obviously something serious had happened but none of us knew or suspected what it was so we kept quiet. The doctor resumed his operation without saying anything, but again he stopped. Turning to the group, he said, "There's been a bad wreck up beyond Harrisburg and a relative of mine is among the badly injured. They want me to come immediately."

Without another word he went back to his operating, one or two of the onlookers gave a nervous cough, but no one said anything. Then the doctor's right-hand man, big, heavy Omar Pancoast who was always present if possible at the Thursday exercises, asked, "Would you like me to scrub up and finish this case, sir?"

The doctor didn't answer immediately, but it was plain that he was dawdling with the operation—and thinking. Finally, his mind evidently made up, he threw down his instruments and, stepping away from the table, said, "I can't finish this case, but I don't want you to go ahead with it, Pancoast. Call Chuck Bond—he was here a few minutes ago—and have him take over." Bells began to tap out the doctor's call, and nurses, orderlies, and doctors dashed out to hurry Chuck in.

"I want you to go with me, Pancoast," Dr. Finney said as the nurses began to divest him of gown, face mask, and gloves. "While I'm changing my clothes I'd like you to get in touch with a local railroad superintendent and have him get a special ready as soon as possible."

"Yes, sir," said Pancoast, and he started away.

"And you, Miss Miles," turning to the head operating-room nurse, "I'd like you to get the emergency trunk out with all instruments, salt solution, other solutions, dressings, and anything else we might need. They didn't say whether there's a hospital there or not so we'll proceed as if there weren't."

"Would you like me to go with you?" Miss Miles asked.

"Certainly would, and one other nurse. Thanks." As he disappeared into the doctors' dressing room, Chuck was just coming out, dressed in white and ready to scrub up and take over the half-finished case.

With Dr. Finney out of hearing the operating room began to hum with conversation only partially hushed and with the noise of nurses, doctors, and orderlies hurrying about gathering up the required paraphernalia for major operative work; but in the midst of it there was one man who sat unperturbed. He was the anesthetist and if, in the excitement, others could give scant thought to the patient lying there unconscious on the table, his operation only half finished, the anesthetist was on the job. Old Griff, as everybody called him—Griffith Davis was his full name—had been at the game too long to be upset by anything, and more clearly than anyone else he realized the danger his patient ran in the prolonged anesthesia that would be necessary. Without orders, therefore, he reduced the amount of ether he was giving to a quantity sufficient only to carry the young man along until adjustments could be made. And there he sat not saying a word, but confident that his charge was all right, until Chuck took over. The staff assistants had quietly kept the gaping wound covered with moist gauze.

When I heard that the Master was going to the wreck with a flock of assistants and nurses and on a special train, all thoughts of the Halsted band went out the window and I made up my mind to get on that train if possible. Man alive! Special train, flying lickety-split to a fearful wreck; excitement; adventure; unusual work; more excitement. I had never seen or experienced anything like that.

Going to the dressing room, I told Dr. Finney how distressed I was over the accident and then said, "Wouldn't you like me to get my new transfusion instrument and go up to the wreck with you?"

"Thanks, old man, but I don't think so."

"I'd be only too happy to go, and if a transfusion were needed I could do it."

"No, I think not. Thanks just the same."

Disconsolately I went back to the operating room and stood watching Chuck skillfully going on with the operation. There was no use asking Dr. Finney a second time; he was an easygoing man and always pleasant but he never liked a fellow to be too persistent.

Chuck was getting along fine and was just about ready for application of the band when Dr. Finney came into the operating room dressed ready to go. Stepping up to the table, he said, "Chuck, I've decided to take you along, after all. Suppose you drop out and let Bernie here"—turning to me—"take over. But hurry up."

So luck was playing into my hands a little, anyhow, and I hurried out to change clothes and scrub up, delighted with the chance to try my skill on a human being. The whole business wouldn't take longer than ten or fifteen minutes, so perfectly had the preliminary preparation been done. Once I got going I had the band applied and was just in the act of tightening it up to the desired degree, perhaps the most important step of all, when back into the operating room, all gowned and gloved again, came Chuck. An assistant standing at my right made way for him, but I was so intent on the work in hand that at first I didn't notice him.

"You're to drop out, Bernie," he said, "and I'll finish up. Dr. Finney wants you to go and get your new transfusion instrument as quickly as you can and meet them at the station. They've already left."

Was that a break! I hopped out of that operating regalia and into my street clothes, and violated all speed laws getting to my office and grabbing the transfusion kit.

But I made the train—just. And what a train it was! Engine,

baggage car, one day coach. But that bobtailed thing was no ordinary train. What it lacked in looks and style and railroad oomph it more than made up in fancy stepping, speed, slam-banging around curves, raucous whistle blowing. Right of way was what we had, and from the very start the engineer opened his throttle wide, hell-bent for his destination. Mile-long freight trains moved to sidings, great and important through passenger trains did likewise, and we could glimpse surprised passengers hanging out of windows as we sped by, screeching and howling but never slowing down.

"Cripes! The guy's gonna kill us all," I yelled to Pancoast, and was not reassured by his answer.

"Looks like it," he yelled back.

Miss Miles smiled a sickly smile. More than once she gave a little gasp as we hit a curve and went ricocheting around the bend.

Even the trainmen seemed uneasy and held onto the sides of their seats as we did. I couldn't laugh even when Miss Miles said she thought it was only Dr. Pancoast's extra weight that held us on the tracks. Dr. Finney was the calmest one among us, but he always was when up against it.

I never did see York, we flew through it so fast, and even when we reached Harrisburg, where I thought we'd surely slow down, that demon engineer went through, I would have sworn, with the wheels of only one side of his train on the tracks. Finally we pulled right up to the wreck. It had occurred on a curve near a little non-descript station, and nearly the whole train had gone over the steep embankment. Fortunately we were near a new and perfectly appointed hospital that some wealthy woman had only recently built, and it was to this that the fifty or so injured and dying were taken, our particular patient among them. We found her in desperate shock and fearfully injured, chiefly about the face and head. It was touch and go for hours as we worked to save her, and only toward midnight was Dr. Finney sure she'd make it. I was

glad he decided against transfusion; he wasn't sure of the intracranial condition.

That interrupted operation on the femoral aneurism† and
certain other blood-vessel operations that later fell to my lot, plus
the occasional appendix and hernia, were the extent of my surgical
achievements before World War I. With this sketchy experience
behind me I don't need to confess that I was far from being an
experienced surgeon when they signed me on with the Johns
Hopkins Hospital Unit, but it was the only possible niche for me
and I seized it. During those grim days at Belleau Wood and
Château-Thierry, working in the front line, often with our own
artillery pounding overhead, operating day and night, night and
day, ceaselessly, interminably, where there were no specialists, no
consultants, I learned more about surgery and gained more confidence than I could have in ten years of ordinary practice.

The war lifted me out of the near-surgeon class and, as a result,
soon after my return to Baltimore I got a hospital service of my
own which, through force of unusual circumstances, gave me an
opportunity to make use of certain executive experience that had
come to me during the war. Interestingly enough, I had asked for
a service in this very institution only a few years before the war
but had been told bluntly to "go out and get a reputation" and then
maybe they'd consider me!

Everything we do costs something. And there always has to
be a first time—whether it's a baby's walking, or a man's taking out
insurance, fighting, or operating—and firsts are usually shaky. So
are seconds and often thirds; in fact, until one gets the hang of
things, insecurity and timidity must be one's portion, and that is
especially true of surgery. Teachers of surgery, supervisors, do
their best to guide their charges' faltering steps, knowing well that

† The patient made a satisfactory recovery.

human beings are the ones who must pay the penalty for mistakes; but there is much that cannot be reduced to absolute positive or negative, much that must be sensed. It is impossible to know for a certainty when a young house officer is ready to handle the knife himself. There is no set time or rule; some boys just naturally "get it" while others don't. Some arrive early, others late, some not at all.

"Here, Bob, you take the knife and open this abdomen," I said to my young assistant early one morning as we stood beside the table ready to begin—and I couldn't help smiling behind my face mask at the sudden, sharp look he gave me and his obvious confusion as he stammered:

"But—"

"You've got to begin sometime, you know," I added before he became too embarrassed, "and you are quite ready."

"You really think so, sir?"

"Yes, but don't let's talk about that now. You come on my side of the table and I'll switch over to yours, and let's go!"

I didn't hurry him exactly but I didn't let him loiter because it was imperative that he have no time to think it over. He was different from some of the others: timid, too cautious, too calculating, and he had said that if it was all right with me he'd rather go slow. All the others wanted just the opposite. I couldn't quite make Bob out. I couldn't help feeling that maybe he was yellow and hadn't the guts, until one day a bit later on, when the strangling baby came in. Without a moment's hesitation Bob grabbed a knife right out of the instrument cabinet and slit her windpipe open and saved her. That was something! He didn't wait to sterilize the knife or call for help or anything else. He just acted, and from that moment it was clear that in him we had a potential surgeon.

No two boys are alike, and the teacher who fails to take note of their differences gets nowhere. Environment, heredity, many factors enter the picture, and as far as possible I tried to study them. As chief surgeon it fell to my lot to choose the boys just out of medical school who were to become house officers on the surgical side.

No one is infallible, and I made my share of mistakes in judgment. You can't tell how a fellow is going to do till he actually gets out on his own, and even then it takes time. One of my boys led me a dog's life and more than once I was on the point of letting him out—even as late as his last year—but each time some little thing came up that stayed my hand. Sometimes he was like a bull in a china shop and would get into bleeding that he should have avoided or tear into tissues in a manner to make one shudder, while the next time he'd do a beautiful operation.

"Look, Fred," I said to him once, "sponge your field clear of blood, like this, and try actually to see the bleeding point before putting on your clamp. Don't grab in the dark, because you might get hold of something you don't want, as you did with that common duct you had hold of yesterday when Dr. Lawson happened to walk into the operating room."

"That was bad, wasn't it?" His frankness in admitting error was a little disarming.

"Sure was, and that's why I'm on the other side of the table today. You've been at the game too long for that and in six months you will be out on your own."

"But the cystic artery can be tough."

"Right, but that's no reason for your going off your head and failing to get it."

"Yes, sir. I'll try to do better."

"Well, let's see you get it this time, and with Frank here acting as your first."

He was a little surprised at that because young Frank Ellsworth was only an interne. Nevertheless he was game, and as I swapped places and became second assistant it soon became apparent that he could do good work if he wanted to. It became equally apparent that young Frank knew how to handle himself for he did measure up to his new job in masterly fashion. We gave him other opportunities later on and were pleased to note continued progress of a kind that assured him promotion at the end of his term.

There was another youngster, though, that I completely lost faith in. He had a lot of knowledge and when I or some staff member worked with him his work was good. Not spectacular, but good. I've often thought he might have got by if he hadn't been so undependable. I suppose you'd call it a moral blind spot, but he couldn't be made to conform. It was hard to make him out.

"Why didn't you wait till Dr. Green got here before going in on that case?" I said to him one morning after a particularly bad performance during the night.

"I did call him."

"But you didn't wait."

"He was held up or something, and the patient was bleeding, and I didn't think he could hold out." He always had an excuse, but this time it didn't work.

"You wouldn't think it was because you wanted to do a major case on your own and this was a good chance?"

"No, sir."

"Well, I do, and you will not become the resident." (He had been substituting.)

"But the patient is in good shape, and—and—"

"And what?" I asked.

The boy was silent.

"We have rules and regulations at this hospital and they are especially specific and rigid about young, inexperienced surgeons like yourself taking matters into their own hands. You have a good mind and perhaps more than average surgical ability but you seem to lack moral responsibility and that makes you a menace to sick people who may be at your mercy. The fact that you apparently got by with last night's operation so far as life is concerned makes no difference whatever. If I can't depend on a man, I don't want him around me, and you fall in that category. Heretofore I have overlooked your delinquencies, thinking that they were due to youth and perhaps enthusiasm, but I find I was mistaken. I'd suggest that you take up some other and less exacting branch of medicine."

Surgery cannot be learned in textbooks. It must be learned by watching and doing, and the teaching is individual. For instance, my first assistant and I, gowned, gloved, and masked, are about to open an abdomen. That is, I do the opening and he does the assisting. This is the way he learns the art of making his fingers think and see and grow as nimble as the digits of Jascha Heifetz. Unlike doctors in the movies and on television a surgeon does not pull his diagnosis out of the air.

A long, smooth cut is made, laying open the skin of the patient's upper right abdomen. Although the case has been studied, it is not entirely clear, and this is an exploratory operation, the final diagnosis to be made as we go along.

"What'd you say that the lady's chief complaint was?" I thought it wise to rehearse the salient features of the case.

"Indigestion, burning pain after eating, nausea."

"Catch that vessel," I interrupt, "and wipe a little faster, so I can see." Then, "Indigestion, pain. Any vomiting or blood?"

"Yes, sir. Once or twice. No blood."

"Jaundice?" I separate the muscle fibers and plump down on the peritoneum.

"No, sir."

"Here, catch that edge." I nick the peritoneum. "Guess the woman's been quite a sufferer—or is it mostly in her head?" enlarging the incision. "Looks all right so far, but we'll soon know. There's the gall bladder poking up. Doesn't look too bad, but"—and here I gently slip my gloved right hand into the abdomen—"I think I'll take a feel all around first." Assistants, nurses, all stand quietly, doing nothing as this goes on—a man, myself, seemingly looking into space, hand in the patient's abdomen halfway up to the elbow, carrying on a monologue aimed at nobody in particular. "Gall bladder's tense and wall's thicker than usual, but I can feel a number of stones. Adherent to surrounding structures. Dense. Nothing in stomach, but we'll take a look at that later." I stop talking momentarily and swish my hand slowly, gently down toward the right side. "Appendix seems bound down a bit. Right ovary O.K., not enlarged. Left ovary's got a little cyst attached to it." For a moment I explore farther. "Both kidneys seem all right, and so's the spleen. Head of the pancreas not hard."

I withdraw my hand. "Let's take a good look at the stomach," I remark, and shove my hand back in, but toward the upper left, and feel around a bit, and then slowly withdraw it, bringing along the body of the stomach itself.

"Take hold, John"—as John, first assistant, substitutes his hand for mine—"and don't let it get away. Looks all right at the pylorus. No ulcers. No growth. But what's this?" I feel along the organ's upper edge and gradually deliver more of it up into view. "A little induration and, yes, I think I can feel the scar of an old healed ulcer. Here, let me hold that and you slide your fingers in there. Feel it?"

"Yes, sir."

"Be sure, now. Describe it."

"Indurated area about an inch in diameter, up high on lesser curvature."

"That's right. Question is: Is that all and is it entirely healed? These things fool you sometimes. How old is she?"

"Fifty-eight, sir, and not very robust."

"Humph. I'd like to look inside that stomach, but guess we'd better give her the benefit of the doubt and just take out the appendix and gall bladder." And at once I begin to mobilize the appendix.

Or, as so often happens, the operation is not exploratory but an emergency in the dead of night. It's that way far too often, and as I step up to the table I can detect grins even through the gauze face masks of nurses and doctors. "Give me a knife now," I usually mumble, "and let's get through this little affair. Gosh, I did hate to get out of bed."

As the incision is made, my assistants bend to clamp bleeding vessels and wipe blood out of the deepening wound.

"Nothing like a McBurney incision for these things, and muscles of kids like this are thin and delicate, easy to separate."

The team is clicking, all hands working smoothly, as if directed by one brain; no one getting in the way of anyone else. Not so simple as it sounds.

"Old Ben [Dr. Crocker] says the child's been sick two days, but they only called him a couple of hours ago. Usual stuff. Put a small retractor in there and another in here. That's it. Now pick up the peritoneum opposite me. Fine."

Carefully nicking the filmy tissue with the sharp edge of my knife, I note the cloudy fluid, possibly full of strep infection, that wells up. I make the opening larger, shift the retractors inside the abdomen, and then carefully, gently, proceed to feel for the appendix.

"Got to go easy in cases like this. I couldn't feel a mass on examination at the home, but the child looked sick; and with temperature, pulse, and leucocytes so high, the appendix is certainly gangrenous, if not ruptured."

Assistants stand by quietly, clamps and gauze in hands, ready for action.

"I feel it; rather tense, adherent, twice normal thickness. Give me a long forceps and a small, moist strip." I withdraw my fingers and prepare to wall off the surrounding gut.

"Think she's busted?" asks the first, deftly placing one end of the sponge down toward the wound, which I widen just a bit to facilitate movements.

"No, but if I'm not careful she will be. Let's have another strip. There. That's it. See her down there?"

"Yes, sir."

"Take a feel," and the first slips the two first fingers of his left hand in.

"You left-handed?"

"No, sir. Why do you ask?"

"Well, it's a funny thing about the sense of touch. Go easy, now, and for Pete's sake don't—"

The first's hand is out before I finish.

Without further ado I slip my own left forefingers down into the wound and work smoothly, deliberately, every once in a while taking a look, now coming completely out and having the first sponge and the second shift his retractor to get more exposure. In short order we have an ominous-looking, markedly swollen, cyanotic, but unruptured appendix exposed and freed for removal.

Nothing is said, except the usual soft-spoken demands for ties, needles and thread, scissors and clamps, until, the tension obviously released, I become a teacher again.

"About that sense of touch, now . . . Here, nurse, give me a continuous suture for the peritoneum . . . Most surgeons find that their sense of touch is not the same in both hands, and when they are up against it and want the utmost delicacy of manipulation, when they desire the nth power of knowledge from feeling, they invariably use the one hand . . . Now for a few interrupteds . . . That's fine . . . And strangely enough, the occasional one like myself, and maybe John—the fellow who does everything right-handed—relies most on his left . . . Ever notice it, John?"

"No, sir. Only now that you mention it, I guess—"

"Would you mind sewing up the skin? Thanks. That's one that's better out than in, and that little excess of exudate we noticed is hardly of any consequence. Give him plenty of fluids, no food, and sedatives as needed."

Since it is night and I have been working all day, I feel close to exhaustion and very much relieved that the emergency operation has gone off without a hitch. I even hum a little as I step away from the table while the nurse unties the strings holding my mask and gown. I slip off the rubber gloves and other paraphernalia, nod to my assistants, and head straight for bed.

It has been my job and that of my staff to give the graduate M.D.'s who are trying to become surgeons a chance to explore the insides of my patients, public and private. On an ordinary day I may perform several such operations, and by the time my assistants have watched and taken part in a few—twenty-five, fifty, perhaps a hundred—they begin to get the hang of things. If the time ever comes when you have to call in a surgeon and you call one who has come in through the front door, you'll be comforted to know that he has spent long years of apprenticeship and has seen and done, again and again, almost everything in the surgical category.

We surgeons who teach doctors to become surgeons lead them by the hand—and I mean that literally. I sometimes actually take my assistant's hand and guide it down to the unseen pathological structures. I want to get him to the point where, by touching the tissue as I do, he can arrive at the same conclusion. I try to develop in him the faculty of diagnosing through his fingertips, even though his hand at the moment may be out of sight. He doesn't reach me for instruction until he has mastered any number of beautifully illustrated six-inch-thick volumes on surgery, complete with footnotes; but we do not learn how to operate from textbooks. I studied pathology before I studied surgery in order to learn what to look for. Young John M.D. will watch and assist, and watch and assist—from the other side of the table—long months before he touches a patient with a knife. His first step in surgery is tying off small blood vessels, and that is important because tying knots is an art in itself. Only when he becomes my first assistant—much, much later—does he assume a responsible part in the team.

When your surgeon operates on you, he doesn't work alone; he works as quarterback, calling the signals to his surgical team. Your surgeon performs the operation, but the first assistant can make it a good or a poor one. If he is clumsy, his hands will get in the way of the operator; in trying to be helpful, he will only hinder. I can usually spot an up-and-coming surgeon by how good he is as first assistant.

With a smoothly working team, in the case of an operation that doesn't develop a sudden hitch, actions are almost automatic and reflex. The surgeon and assistants can perform a competent job and yet be talking at the same time—and not always of the case in hand. Every operation is also a demonstration, and since there are always some kibitzers—students, staff members, visiting physicians and surgeons, sometimes as numerous as at a pinochle game—during a lull in the action some of them, properly gowned and masked, may even be invited to step up to the operating table for a close-up, intimate view of structures and operative steps.

There comes a time in many operations—usually along toward the end, after the main steps have been taken and the tension has been relieved and only the so-called closure remains—when surgeons, assistants, and sometimes nurses and onlookers begin a running conversation. It was on one of these occasions when I was watching Professor Halsted operate that the professor and his first seemed especially engrossed, and though they had much to say to each other, it was all *sotto voce*, and no one else heard a word. The entire audience was desperately interested, as it always was in anything the professor had to say. I felt he was discussing some fine points that he didn't want us to hear, and was slightly piqued.

Later I waylaid the resident and asked him what in the world the conversation was about and why the secrecy.

"Did you see Strangler Lewis wrestle last night?" he asked.

"Yes, I was there."

"Well, the professor was there, too. He thinks Lewis is a darn good wrestler, but he didn't like the way he was using the toe hold. He was discussing the toe hold and the ethics of using the toe hold all the time."

But don't worry—the surgeon takes it easy only when everything is under control. Let something go wrong, a sudden emergency, an unexpected slip—a hemorrhage resulting from a broken thread—and in a flash hands that were moving slowly and deliberately in normal fashion take on almost blinding speed; rhythm gives way to the jerky motions needed to grasp new and different instruments hastily handed him. At every operation we have ready and waiting many more instruments than needed—just in case. The running conversation ceases; the nurses and orderlies stand hushed and tense. At such times one man, and one man only, speaks. His words are sharp and staccato, but his voice is never raised. He is master of himself and the situation, and it is the surgeon who, with all the responsibility, still steadies the rest of the team.

The moment the emergency has been dealt with successfully, you can practically hear the relaxation of tension, and once again normal conversation is resumed.

"Ligature slipped over the end of that vessel down there," said my own chief, after a well-remembered episode, "and that's a good lesson for you fellows. The only man who has no accidents is the one who does no operating. I preach and shall continue to preach that every effort should be made to keep out of trouble, for the simple reason that it is easier to keep out than to get out after you have once got in. This is a lesson in point, and since the patient might have died then and there, I doubt if any of you will forget it."

He was right. And that's one way your surgeon learns—by emergencies.

The better hospitals work on a process of rigid elimination. A graduate M.D. who aspires to surgery goes through four stages —interne, second assistant, first assistant, and resident. His surgical work takes four years in addition to his regular four years in the medical school. Let us say that a given hospital has twenty internes. Out of these we may select two or three to remain on for an additional year as second assistants, and when that year is completed the one or two best of the three are kept on a third year as first assistants, with the fourth and final year going to the one who appears to be most apt. This man becomes the resident surgeon, so called, and is taught actual operating. In larger hospitals there may be two or more such residents, one for each service.

These men are good and they have a hard row to hoe. We have to be tough. We eliminate many good men, and sometimes make glaring mistakes. I remember one aspirant. We all thought he was good, and so did he, until one day an emergency arose, and he did an operation on his own without the direct supervision of his chief, a most unusual occurrence. At that, he might have got by if a junior staff man hadn't happened to wander into the operating room and notice the excessive bleeding the patient was having.

"If the youngster had only been sweating, I wouldn't have thought so much of it," the doctor reported.

He almost had us fooled. But when the chips were down, he couldn't come through. He didn't act—or react—like a surgeon. At the end of an operation, even a minor operation, most surgeons are drenched with sweat, from inner tension. The operator who doesn't sweat over a job, especially when he gets into trouble, generally hasn't got it in him to be a surgeon.

We who teach young men to become surgeons lead them slowly, gradually, carefully, inculcating in them gentleness and respect for tissues and the need for conserving blood. In an efficient operation there is very little bleeding; this is accomplished by a system of applying clamps—sometimes there may be two dozen or even more in a wound. The assistants do this as the surgeon cuts, and later on these clamps are removed by tying with silk or catgut the little points they hold. This sounds very simple, and it is—to the one who knows how to tie knots. I practiced the art hours and hours, using up miles of light and heavy thread on the arms of chairs.

In the critical operation, especially if the blood vessel lies deep, most surgeons tie their own knots. The old-fashioned granny knot is the stand-by and is usually tied triple, but the art comes in tying the second knot, because that is the one that most often breaks. We go to great lengths teaching assistants to tie good knots, because if one slips or breaks after the clamp has been removed, a serious hemorrhage may occur before the clamp can be reapplied.

One young surgeon learned a valuable lesson through the recurrence of a hernia before the patient got off the operating table. The young operator had done the operation very well, and the nurse in charge told me she had never seen a hernia job done more smoothly. But in his enthusiasm to do an especially fine job, the operator tied fancy knots and had the anesthetic discontinued a little too early; the patient began to wake up, gave a little cough—then a bigger one—and there, larger than life, was the telltale swelling in the groin, just as it had been before. The knots had not held.

The staff surgeon sent in to take over made the youngster open up the wound and clean out the bits of thread that lay loose in it. Then, using the old reliable granny knots, he did the usual repair—and one young man learned a valuable lesson, while the patient suffered no other harm than spending a little extra time on the table. A half-dozen visiting experts witnessed the episode, and that was good, too, because a man, especially a surgeon, has to learn how to take it and like it.

After a young man has proved himself by assisting in a variety of operations and seems ready to handle the knife himself, we select a few simple cases of the "less major" type and, instead of his assisting us, we assist him. In this manner the welfare of the patient is secured and the young operator is given the confidence needed, for it is one thing to assist, quite another to operate. We guide him and, experienced in teaching, lead him to think he is making all the decisions and doing all the work. It is a trying time and many a man is made or broken at that point.

Once the budding surgeon gets hold of himself, we, the teachers, drop out of his operations and let one of his confreres take our place as assistant. This puts him on his own, but it does not mean that we give him free rein. To do so would be unjust to the patient, and so we stand by and watch or perhaps go to the doctors' room for a smoke. This all makes for confidence, and as time passes and operations succeed operations—with the major succeeding the relatively minor—we give the impression that all supervision is off, while having a younger staff man wander in occasionally and seemingly accidentally, and slowly, gradually note and take pride in the development of yet another surgeon who can be trusted.

At that, though, the new brother isn't a finished product, and nobody knows it better than himself. It is results that count in surgery, as in all things, and so, as our protégé begins to operate, we scan his cases with an eagle eye to see how well they do after operation, whether they have smooth or stormy convalescence, whether their wounds heal as they should or become infected,

whether they are cured of the affection for which they have been
operated on or are benefited as much as they should be. In short,
there is a balance sheet, but in its review we recognize again that
the only man who gets no bad results or has no deaths is the one
who does no operations.

Surgeons, the last people to take their own medicine, often
josh each other about the fact, reciting their various ailments,
together with remedies wondrous and bizarre. Never, though,
have I been more amused than when I saw one of America's well-
known wielders of the knife stop in the midst of removing two
thirds of a man's stomach because of ulcers and receive a glass
of milk, through a tube proffered by a nurse, for his own ulcer.

Spare Parts
for Defective Hearts
by Ben Pearse

In 1846 Dr. Ephraim MacDowell dared to enter one of the deep cavities of the human body to remove a tumor and save a woman's life. Mobs rioted around his home, and had his patient died, he would have been accused of murder. Since then one organ after another has surrendered to the surgeon's scalpel. Operations unheard of a decade ago are now being performed with routine regularity. The heart itself has been opened and its defects remedied. The selection that follows is one example in a dazzling array of surgical accomplishments. Nor is the end in sight. We may hope that in the not-too-distant future many defective parts of the body will be replaced from banks of healthy organs similar to the blood banks which already exist.

Frank S. Costa is one of thousands of clerks in the post office that covers four square blocks in midtown New York. He bangs away at a typewriter, wrestles voluminous files, and whips around on office tasks eight hours a day. Night and morning he bucks the rush-hour subway crowds commuting to and from his home in the Bronx. To watch him, you'd never suspect one of his heart valves is artificial.

Two years ago Frank Costa was about to lose his job because pounding a typewriter actually winded him. Ordinary office routine set his heart to throbbing as though he were performing heavy manual labor. When I asked him about the operation that had saved his job and possibly his life, he told me, "You'd never think a little plastic gadget no bigger than a man's thumb and shorter could make all that difference."

The ailment that threatened to make an invalid of Mr. Costa at thirty-nine is known medically as aortic insufficiency. In lay terms, that means a leaky heart valve. The aorta, the body's largest blood vessel, receives the freshly oxygenated blood from the heart and distributes it through smaller vessels throughout the body. In the normal person, a valve at the base of the aorta, where it leads off from the left ventricle, closes after each contraction or beat, holding the blood in the circulatory system while the ventricle is filling again for another beat. But when the fragile valve leaves are thickened or misshapen by disease, they can't close completely. Some blood leaks back into the ventricle after each beat.

The direct result is an inadequate supply of blood, and the life-giving oxygen it carries, to all the body tissues. One indirect result is that the heart muscle has to work harder and faster to make up for the slippage of the leaky valve. Another is that the ventricle becomes enlarged to accommodate the backflow from the aorta in addition to the normal flow from the left auricle and the lungs. There are other complications, but overwork and enlargement are usually enough in time to tire the heart to the point of quitting.

Sometimes the condition goes undetected for many years. When the leak is small, the victim may not even notice any effect beyond a feeling of fatigue or shortness of breath after moderate exertion. Frank Costa remembers an illness while he was in high school. If it was rheumatic fever—the disease is often difficult to diagnose—he suffered no apparent ill effects. Many victims do not. He worked in a shipyard during World War II and got an appointment as a letter carrier in 1947. He walked his route for seven years before the leaky valve seemed suddenly to get worse. When walking became difficult, he was transferrred to clerical duty, but that helped only temporarily. "It's hard to believe," Mr. Costa told me, "but I used to get out of breath just pushing a pencil."

One of the specialists he consulted, Dr. Robert Lloyd Segal, told him about a new operation being performed in Washington, D.C., by Dr. Charles A. Hufnagel, professor of surgery at Georgetown University Hospital. The operation was known by the formidable title, "Surgical correction of aortic insufficiency by implantation of a plastic prosthesis." What that boils down to is inserting an artificial valve in the aorta to prevent the blood, or most of it, from flowing the wrong way back into the heart. Dr. Hufnagel had performed the operation on a human patient for the first time in September, 1952, after many experimental operations on animals. The results were successful and since then he had performed many more to install what had come to be known as the "Hufnagel valve."

Dr. Segal showed Mr. Costa a picture of one, a transparent plastic tube about an inch in diameter and an inch and one half long. It had a bulge in the middle to accommodate the plastic ball inside that allowed the blood to flow only in one direction. A segment of the aorta is removed, Dr. Segal explained, and replaced by the plastic tube in much the same way that you mend a garden hose. The ends of the aorta are clamped onto the tube with nylon rings, so that they won't slip off under pressure of the pulse beat.

The man-made valve, Dr. Segal told his patient, would not entirely correct the backflow. For various reasons, the valve is inserted not at the site of the defective valve, but several inches "downstream" after the aorta has arched upward over the heart and is descending behind it, between the heart and the spine. In

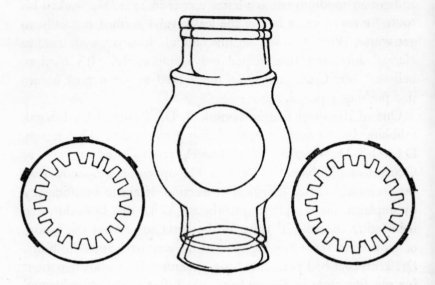

In the middle is the plastic valve devised by Dr. Charles A. Hufnagel. Inside it is the silicone ball which controls the blood flow. The nylon fixation rings on either side seal the ends of the patient's artery to the valve openings.

that position, the artificial valve prevents backflow from the 70 per cent of the body's circulatory system that is below the arm level. With only the backflow from the arteries leading to the head and arms—the other 30 per cent—to cope with, the heart can manage. Dr. Segal pointed out that with reasonable success Mr. Costa could expect to go back to work again.

"When they mentioned going back to work," Mr. Costa said, "I could hardly wait to get on with the operation. I was only thirty-nine then. The thought of my wife, Ida, having to take care of me and our three girls—Mary Ann, Elaine, and Denise— the rest of my life was pretty discouraging."

Mr. Costa entered Georgetown University Hospital in May, 1956, and a few days later Dr. Hufnagel installed one of his plastic valves. The recovery was uneventful. After returning home in June, Mr. Costa rested to regain his strength. Then he went back to his job in October and has been working steadily ever since.

"I feel well enough to walk a route again," he said, "but the doctors tell me to let well enough alone and stay in the office. With my artificial valve, I'm expecting to live to a ripe old age."

Aortic insufficiency is one of the more common heart defects. Statistics in this field are meager, but one estimate places the annual incidence at about 65,000 victims, although the sample on which that figure is based is too small to make it more than a guess. Many of those cases are not serious enough to require medical attention and are not reported. Some that are serious enough to be diagnosed can be treated by restricting the victim's physical activity. At Georgetown University Hospital the practice is not to recommend the valve implantation unless the defect is actually producing some disability in the patient, or unless it is becoming worse and threatens to become disabling.

"A patient with a mild aortic insufficiency," Dr. Hufnagel explained, "may live many years without experiencing serious difficulty. Even if the defect shows definite indications of worsening, the artificial valve is not the only surgical remedy. A 70-per-cent correction is a compromise, and sometimes direct repair of the valve itself is feasible.

"However, we do not believe in saving the implantation as a last resort. The operative risk in our experience has been directly proportional to the status of the disease—the more advanced it is, the higher the risk. Age and other factors enter in, but, generally speaking, the best results are obtained before the damage has been allowed to progress to the terminal stage. Our operative mortality has been less than 15 per cent; including several terminal cases among the first series of operations six years ago."

Of some 500 plastic heart valves serving their human hosts

to date, more than two hundred of them have been installed by Dr. Hufnagel himself, the vast majority successfully. That means the patient not only survived but was measurably benefited, usually to the extent of being able to resume work on a somewhat reduced scale. At first patients came to Georgetown University Hospital from all parts of the United States and several foreign countries. Some still do. But the Hufnagel valve implantation is now being performed at medical centers from Sweden to Australia, Japan to South Africa. The Brunswick Manufacturing Company, of Quincy, Massachusetts, which worked closely with Dr. Hufnagel, lists four valve sizes in its surgical-supply catalogue, ranging from three quarters of an inch to one and one-eighth inches in diameter. The price, $121, includes two multiple-point fixation rings—tough, braided nylon rings with stainless-steel teeth around their inner circumference—to clamp the aorta on at each end.

While aortic insufficiency is frequently owing to some type of infection, the most common cause is rheumatic fever. Miss Violet Winter, a librarian in the Treasury Department in Washington, for example, was stricken while in her teens. Though she recovered after a siege of several weeks, her heart, principally the aortic valve, had been seriously affected. The doctors warned that her future would have to be as sedentary as she could make it.

Miss Winter took a course in library administration and got a job at the Treasury Department. By conserving her strength, she managed pretty well for several years. But the Treasury library walls are lined with shelves up to the ceiling. Reaching the topmost shelves meant climbing ladders. As time went on she found herself carrying fewer and fewer books at a time. More and more frequently she had to ask someone else to return volumes to the top shelves. Unhappy about not being able to do her job, she went to her doctor for advice. After an examination, he told her he believed a Hufnagel valve would help.

"I knew there was some risk involved," Miss Winter explained, "and I thought about it for some time. But I couldn't even keep up with the housework in my efficiency apartment. I had to give up teaching Sunday school and spend weekends in bed resting. Life was getting to be such a chore that I decided to take whatever small risk might be involved."

Since Dr. Hufnagel operated on Miss Winter in October, 1956, the change has been remarkable, according to Miss Isabella S. Diamond, chief librarian. "You'd never know Violet was the same person," she said. "We were always glad to help her; she had a wonderful disposition even when she was tired. But now she won't let us do a thing for her. She climbs ladders with an armful of books as though she never had heart trouble."

I had heard that the first valves used in the operation made a slight click. But even in the quiet of the library I could hear none, although I was sitting beside Miss Winter's desk. When I mentioned it, she laughed. "My friends all seem to be surprised," she said, "when they don't hear me ticking like a clock. Would you like to listen?" Pressing my ear to the middle of the left side of her back, I could hear nothing unusual except perhaps a slight accent to the heartbeat.

"Dr. Hufnagel told me," she said, "that he's using a different material for the ball of the valve than he did. And he wrapped something around the valve before he stitched me up. I'm so well muffled I can't even hear it myself."

Even when an operation has been performed hundreds of times, it can never be called "routine" if it involves the heart or major blood vessels. Diagnostic techniques are so highly developed today that the surgeon knows almost exactly the condition he will find and what he plans to do to correct it. But though the heart has proved to be one of the toughest organs in the body, it can also be temperamental. Dr. Hufnagel's team— six doctors and two nurses—that implanted a valve in the aorta of a forty-year-old man at Georgetown University Hospital a few weeks ago had performed the same operation dozens of times. But as I watched, I could feel an air of tension.

The patient was already on the operating table when I entered Operating Room No. 3—Dr. Hufnagel's—at 7:30 A.M., clad in the green cotton pajamas, cap, and gauze mask that are required costume even for observers. From a low balcony at one end of the room I watched the electrodes of the EKG—short for electro-cardiograph—machine being attached to the wrists and ankles, and the mask for the anesthetic being fitted.

At eight-fifteen the door opened and Dr. Hufnagel appeared. He is a man of medium height and rather slight build, with short, wiry black hair that heightens his youthful appearance—he is only forty-one. With a word of greeting and a few questions about the patient's condition, he went through a rigorous scrubbing routine before donning his surgical gown, gloves, and mask. Assuring himself everything was in order, he stepped to the side of the operating table behind the patient, who was lying on his right side. Dr. Hufnagel motioned me to a low footstool behind him and his assistant, Dr. Alberto Villegas, so that I could see over their shoulders without interfering with their movements. At the head of the table was the anesthesiologist, Dr. Thomas F. McDermott. Across the table stood Dr. Thomas C. Lee, the resident surgeon, and his assistant, Dr. Gerald Hogan. An intern and the two nurses completed the team. At eight forty-six Dr. Hufnagel took his scalpel and made an incision almost the length of the sixth rib, about four inches below the left armpit.

An estimate that surgeons spend half their operating-room lives tying knots wouldn't be far wrong. The incision across the intercostal muscles covering the ribs had severed perhaps a hundred small blood vessels. Each of the severed ends had first to be clamped to halt the blood flow, then tied with a silk thread and a double knot. That tedious task completed, the rib was removed, and the thin, translucent membrane that lines the chest cavity was cut, exposing the left lung. Since the lung covered the heart and the aorta in this position, it had to be partly deflated and pushed toward the front wall of the chest cavity. This called for a delicate adjustment of respiration by the anesthesiologist— more oxygen and less anesthetic to compensate for the reduced air volume. While Dr. McDermott manipulated valves of the steel oxygen and cyclopropane tanks at his elbow, Dr. Hufnagel watched the EKG machine. The tiny blobs of light gliding across the equator of the oscilloscope told him the heart rhythm was within normal limits.

When the lungs had been pushed forward, exposing the heart, the first element of the diagnosis was confirmed: edema (an accumulation of body fluids) of the pericardium, the sac enveloping the heart. Normally, this sac fits as tightly as the shell fits an egg. This accumulation of fluids between the heart and its covering was making it more difficult for the already overburdened muscle to perform its pumping function. A small incision was made in the sac, and the fluid was quickly drained off. With the pericardium back to normal size, the descending aorta, so called because it leads downward to the abdomen and legs, was exposed to view.

It was easy to see now why Dr. Hufnagel had chosen the place he had for insertion of the artificial valve. The base of the aorta, the site of the defective natural valve, is in constant motion, bobbing and twisting with each contraction of the left ventricle. But after the aorta has arched over the top of the heart and turns downward toward the abdomen, it is relatively stable. The only movement is a slight expansion and contraction with each heartbeat; stress and strain on the plastic-tube connections will be at a minimum. For that and other more technical reasons, the chosen position gives the greatest benefit with the least risk.

To free a section of the aorta about four inches long from the tissues surrounding it involves more knot tying before the two fixation rings can be fitted in place. The rings are split, so that they can be slipped around the aorta before it is cut, and are grooved around their outer circumference to hold the silk ligatures that will tie them shut at the proper time. In the two stainless-steel teeth at either side of the split are tiny holes, so that the ring can be tied shut with steel wire as well as silk ligatures, double assurance that it will stay in place.

Up to this time Dr. Hufnagel had kept up a running fire of conversation with the members of his surgical team to hold their undivided attention, even during the tedious knot-tying business. Now he was silent as he reached for the holder with the valve in its claws. The valve is as smooth as meticulous polishing with jewelers' rouge can make it. After soaking for eighteen hours in a sterilizing solution, it was triple-rinsed before being placed on a tray beside the operating table. Dr. Hufnagel rinsed it again for good measure, shook it to be sure the ball was rolling free, and turned back to his patient. Not knowing just how close I would be permitted to stand, I had brought a pair of opera glasses with me. When I raised them to my eyes, it was almost like looking through a microscope. In this limited field of vision you couldn't distinguish one pair of gloved hands from another, so swiftly did they move. Hardly a word was spoken.

First, a clamp was placed "upstream" from the segment—about the size of a frankfurter—which had been raised free of the surrounding tissues. Just an inch or so above this clamp the artery branching off the aorta to the left arm continued to pulsate rhythmically. Next, another clamp was placed across the "downstream" end of the segment, and the new, artificial valve was placed alongside the portion in between to serve as a measuring guide. If too long a piece were removed, the ends of the severed artery wouldn't reach. If the piece removed were

too short, the valve would be thrown out of alignment. Even
the slightest angle at the junction could cause clotting. Two
carefully gauged snips of a pair of scissors, and a section exactly
the right length was excised.

Now the downstream end of the severed artery was held wide
open with pronged tweezers while the valve was inserted.
Quickly the nylon fixation ring was fitted around it, and held
shut with a clamp while the silk ligature was tied. As the other
end of the valve was inserted into the upstream end of the
aorta, the valve was filled to overflowing with a saline solution—
containing a small quantity of anticoagulant—to prevent any air
from getting into the blood stream. Air bubbles may cause complications. In a moment the upper fixation ring was tied in place
and the downstream clamp was removed.

The little white silicone ball was clearly visible in the transparent saline solution that filled its cage. I watched, fascinated, as
the upper clamp was opened, very slowly to prevent a sudden
surge. At the first tinge of pink the ball rolled toward the tiny
flanges that prevented it from seating, or closing, at the downstream end, and nestled there until the blood flow, getting redder
and redder, hid it from view. When the upper clamp had been
entirely removed, and the aorta above and below the tube resumed its measured, rhythmic pulsing, I could only imagine the
ball shuttling back and forth, back and forth, with each beat of
the heart. I looked up at the clock. The blood flow had been
halted for three minutes and twenty-nine seconds. I knew I
hadn't held my breath all that time, but I felt as though I had. It
seemed a little like watching life begin again.

The steel "safety" ligatures still had to be secured in the fixation rings. A narrow mesh cuff would be sutured around both
ends to keep the aorta snugly against the tubing and prevent
clotting. And there were many more knots to be tied before the

chest cavity could be closed and the tissues stitched together again. But somehow you felt sure everything was going to be all right now, that a new lease on life had just been granted.

The actual installation of the valve had taken about three and one-half minutes, the operation nearly three and one-half hours. Afterward, as we walked back to the locker room to change into street clothes, I asked Dr. Hufnagel how he happened to invent this tiny plastic gadget that had meant so much to so many persons suffering from leaky heart valves. It looked so simple, yet I knew it must have taken years of patient work to perfect.

"Happen to," Dr. Hufnagel said with a laugh, repeating my own phrase, "is the right way to put it. I started out trying to transplant a kidney in an experimental animal. One thing led to another until one day the valve idea was staring me in the face." The story I gathered from Dr. Hufnagel, some of his colleagues, and sundry medical reports goes like this.

The inspiration to enter the medical profession in the first place came from his late father, a physician and surgeon in Richmond, Indiana, where Dr. Hufnagel was born and reared. He took his undergraduate medical course at the University of Notre Dame, and when he entered the Harvard Medical School in 1937, had already decided to become a surgeon. His determination to concentrate on cardiovascular surgery—that involving the heart and large blood vessels—was the first instance of "happenstance."

One of his professors at Harvard was the brilliant Dr. Robert E. Gross, who in 1938—while Dr. Hufnagel was a student in one of his classes—performed the first successful operation to correct a congenital defect known as "patent ductus arteriosus." Before birth, a small blood vessel—the ductus arteriosus—shunts the blood stream around the lungs. Normally, after birth, the duct closes, but in about one child in every 2,000 births it remains patent, or open, permitting venous blood to escape into the arterial system. Death in infancy was the usual result. Adults with this affliction were rare—before the operation in which Dr. Gross corrected the defect by cutting the ductus and sewing up the two ends.

"The patent ductus operation today is not considered much more serious than a hernia operation," Dr. Hufnagel explained. "But when Dr. Gross first performed it in 1938, operations on the heart or large blood vessels around it were taboo except perhaps in an emergency—say, stitching up a stab wound. That Gross operation proved that operations on or about the human heart could be done successfully. Even we students recognized that it was the beginning of a new era in surgery. I wanted to take part in it."

Dr. Gross later performed other milestone operations, and in one of them his former student, Dr. Hufnagel, played a supporting role. After being graduated from Harvard Medical School in 1941, he was appointed Arthur Tracey Cabot Fellow at the Surgical Research Laboratory, which happened to be across the street from the Boston Children's Hospital, where Dr. Gross was on the surgery staff. Since they were both experimenting with transplantation of organs and blood vessels, they decided to collaborate in a series of experiments that led up to the first reported operation to correct a relatively common vascular defect, a coarctation, or narrowing, of the aorta.

Coarctations vary considerably in length, but are often as short and sharp as the waist of an hourglass. If only a short segment had to be removed, they believed, the aorta would stretch enough for the ends to be stitched together to restore the blood flow. After they had proved their hypothesis in experimental tests on animals, Dr. Gross performed his first successful correction of this defect on July 6, 1945, on a twelve-year-old girl. The Gross-Hufnagel report was published first, but it developed later that Drs. Clarence Crafoord and G. Nylin, working independently, had performed a similar operation in Stockholm, Sweden, in October, 1944, although owing to the war conditions their report was not published until long afterward.

That took care of short coarctations. If the narrowing were longer than a fraction of an inch, however, as many are, a graft of some kind would be needed to replace it. Many solid materials had been tried—gold, silver, and glass, coated inside with paraffin —and all discarded because they caused the blood to clot. Experimenting with new plastics developed during World War II, Dr. Hufnagel found one, methyl methacrylate, in a form known as Plexiglas, that didn't have a clotting effect. But then he ran into another difficulty. When he replaced a segment of aorta with a plastic tube, he tied a silk ligature around each end to hold the aorta onto the tube. The ligature shut off the circulation, and the tissues beyond it died and sloughed away. With nothing to hold it, the aorta slipped off under pressure of the pulse beat, causing a hemorrhage.

To correct that, Dr. Hufnagel designed his multiple-point fixation ring, which is as essential to the operation as the valve. The silk ligature is tied not around the aorta itself, but around a nylon ring made slightly larger than the aorta, so that it does not actually touch the tissues at all. The teeth around the ring's inner circumference penetrate and hold the aorta on. But the spaces between them allow enough circulation to keep the tissues beyond the ring alive and healthy. It is a triumph in surgical ingenuity.

Although he reported the successful implantation of plastic tubes with the fixation rings in experimental animals in 1947, he used them on only a few human patients. Homografts, vessels preserved from deceased donors, were proving much better adapted than a solid material, especially if the graft had to be several inches long. But then it occurred to him that if the body could accommodate itself to a short tube, it might also tolerate a tube with a ball inside, a valve. And a plastic valve opened up new possibilities.

"I just kept turning it over and over in my mind," Dr. Hufnagel recalled, "and I finally decided to see if it wouldn't work."

He began his new departure in heart surgery while he was still at Harvard, and continued it after he took his present post at Georgetown University in 1950.

The success of this first implantation of an artificial organ with a moving part in the human body has stimulated widespread interest in this field. While surgery has made great strides in recent years in correcting many types of heart ailments, the present method of placing an artificial valve at some distance from the natural aortic valve has its limitations. Dr. Hufnagel is only one of several who are now experimenting with various kinds of artificial valves to be implanted in the heart itself as replacements. In Detroit, Dr. James H. Wible and his associates at Wayne State University College of Medicine designed a "watch-spring flap" to correct a leaky mitral valve, the valve separating the left auricle and ventricle. Made of a watch-spring alloy wire covered with nylon, the first valve implanted in a human patient was recently reported functioning successfully more than a year after the operation. With open-heart surgery, plastic-sponge patches are frequently used to close up holes inside the heart.

At the National Heart Institute in Bethesda, Maryland, Dr. Stanley J. Sarnoff has been working with a modification of the Hufnagel valve to correct a rather common defect, aortic stenosis, a constriction of the valve that cuts down the blood flow from the heart. While various operations to widen the valve opening have proved helpful, Dr. Sarnoff's approach is to implant a plastic valve by-passing the constricted organ in order to bring the blood flow up to normal volume. It has been tested successfully on experimental animals, and with some modifications is believed to offer possibilities for avoiding the necessity for operating on the valve itself.

Other researchers have gone even further. At the annual meeting of the American Society for Artificial Internal Organs in Philadelphia in April, one section of the program was devoted to a discussion of implanting not only artificial valves but also entire hearts and kidneys to replace defective natural organs. Artificial heart and kidney machines are getting to be part of any modern hospital's equipment. Models small enough to be implanted in the human body present formidable problems, but none that those participating in the discussion seemed to think couldn't be surmounted in time. In fact, models of implantable hearts and kidneys actually have been made, and some have been tried experimentally in animals. Since Dr. Hufnagel was one of the panelists, I asked what he thought the prospects were.

"Certainly we'll be able to implant artificial organs—someday," he said. "I've been working on an artificial heart myself. But it's going to take considerable time and money, and meanwhile other developments offer more immediate promise. We have already installed aortic and mitral valves at the normal site in experimental animals that have been functioning for more than a year, and other laboratories are working along similar lines. They should be ready for use in humans before very long. As techniques in open-heart surgery improve, replacement of defective valves may soon be no more serious than the patent ductus operation. In fact, surgical procedures are available now for almost all cardiovascular defects in properly selected cases. The progress being made in applying these procedures to an ever-widening selection of patients indicates that surgery will correct most of the mechanical defects that have made up such a large part of our heart-disease mortality in the past."

ADVENTURES
IN THE MODERN WORLD

Navy Doctor in Laos

by Thomas A. Dooley

The present-day experiences of Dr. Tom Dooley offer a graphic example of the gulf that still exists between scientific medicine and superstition.

Despite the difficulties under which he labored, Dr. Dooley made use of the latest methods of diagnosis, treated patients with the most recently developed drugs, did his best to explain to them the importance of scientific standards of sanitation and nutrition, and, above all, brought to his work the compassion which is the noblest mark of the dedicated physician. Opposed to him was the belief in magical cures from which Western man has freed himself. Dr. Tom Dooley is one of many medical heroes, some virtually unknown and others as famous as Dr. Schweitzer, who in many cases are laying down their lives to aid the ignorant, the poverty-stricken, and the oppressed.

High above the Pacific, flying westward in a luxury air liner, the night passes swiftly. Passengers put away their books and brief cases; one by one the reading lights wink out.

But I am the sleepless traveler, my mind filled with memories that are more captivating than dreams. I close my eyes and recall that wretched refugee camp in Haiphong (North Vietnam) in the spring of '55. Operation Cockroach the Navy called us—one young Navy doctor, still professionally wet behind the ears; four young enlisted men who had only a few months' training as hospital

corpsmen; and a half-million filthy, diseased, mutilated Asians fleeing from the godless cruelties of communism.

We had seen simple, tender, loving care—the crudest kind of
medicine inexpertly practiced by mere boys—change a people's fear
and hatred into friendship and understanding. We had witnessed
the power of medical aid to reach the hearts and souls of a nation.
We had seen it transform the brotherhood of man from an ideal
into a reality that plain people could understand.

To me that experience was like the white light of revelation. It
made me proud to be a doctor. Proud to be an American doctor
who had been privileged to witness the enormous possibilities of
medical aid in all its Christlike power and simplicity.

I preached so ardently that my folks began to worry. "Look,
Dooley," my friends would say, "you've had adventure enough.
When are you going to settle down?" My mother reminded me
of all the things I had always wanted, and now might have. A
home, a wife, kids, a nice medical practice, maybe a few fine hunting horses. My old medical mentor told me I'd better get on with
my postgraduate training if I hoped to be a good orthopedic
surgeon.

How could I make them see that things would never be the
same?

One evening in February, 1956, after I had been home from
Asia only a few months, I went to a dinner at the Vietnamese
Embassy in Washington, D.C. This night I had a premonition that
all hope of returning to Indochina with a medical team of my
own would hinge on whatever happened at that dinner.

My good friend, Ambassador Tran Van Chuong of Vietnam,
had arranged a dinner party for me to which he had invited a
number of Cambodian and Laotian diplomats. Late that evening I
was still talking about the kind of medical mission I had in mind—
small, privately financed (mostly out of my own pocket), without
any government or church sponsorship or obligations. The team

would consist only of myself and a few of the young Americans who had served with me in North Vietnam. I saw that the Laotian ambassador, the Honorable Ourot Souvannavong, was following me with keen interest.

"But, Dr. Dooley," he asked, "why should you, a young man just released from your naval duty, with a career before you, choose to make this sacrifice? Obviously you have much to offer. But what do you stand to gain?"

Once more I tried to explain my deep conviction that medical aid, offered on a people-to-people basis, could form lasting bonds of friendship between East and West. If this was true, we American doctors had a duty to perform. Since I had served in Southeast Asia and had seen the need, the duty for me as an individual was inescapable. Besides, I was young, unattached, free to go wherever I was needed

Suddenly I remembered something that big, hard-boiled Boatswain's Mate Norman Baker had once said in answer to a somewhat similar question. Gambling on my ability to translate Baker's homespun American into French, I explained how Baker had groped for words to explain our motives, and then blurted out:

"Aw, sir, we just want to do what we can for people who ain't got it so good!"

The Cambodians raised their eyebrows and smiled—Baker's words had hit the mark. But Ambassador Souvannavong beamed, and from the way he shook his head in frank admiration I could practically read his mind: These incredible Americans!

"Dr. Dooley," he said, "my country would be honored to receive your mission."

All along I had been counting on Norman Baker, Peter Kessey, and Dennis Shepard, the most devoted and dependable of the enlisted men who had been with me in North Vietnam. This wasn't going to be easy. Denny Shepard, newly married, was taking his premed at the University of Oregon. Pete Kessey was attending pharmacy school in Austin, Texas. Baker, also a bridegroom, was still in the Navy. Would they as civilians return to that part of Asia where they had seen such wretchedness?

However, Pete and Denny responded to my call promptly and enthusiastically. Baker's ship was somewhere at sea; several weeks passed before I could get in touch with him. Then one day, in Washington, I received a long-distance call from Baker in San Diego. When I told him about Operation Laos, his roar could be heard from coast to coast, even without the help of A.T.&T.

"What! Back to Indochina? Are you crazy? Why, you slave-driving fool—sir—you couldn't pay me to go back into that hole! Besides, my wife wouldn't stand for it! No—not a chance!"

There was an awkward silence. I just let him simmer down. Then:

"Hello . . . You still there, Doc? Listen, you don't really need *me*, do you? What makes you think we can do any real good out there? And there's something you seem to have forgotten. (*Hearty chuckle.*) Little Old Baker is still the pride and joy of Uncle Sam's Navy!"

I assured him that I needed him, that Operation Laos was a big challenge, and that I was pretty sure I could get him out of the Navy on an early discharge. I could hear him grumbling and moaning.

"Aw, Doc, sure, I *volunteer!* But Priscilla's going to divorce me for this sure as shootin'!"

(Bless her heart, Priscilla Baker did nothing of the sort. She went right ahead with a project I didn't know about at the time—having their baby.)

The huge Vietnamese cargo plane made three trips to Vientiane with our four tons of crates and packing cases. We went in on the last flight, made a perilous landing on the steel-mat runway, and climbed down bone-tired after six hours perched atop packing cases. While a small army of coolies unloaded, we piled our essential gear into an antiquated truck and headed into town.

Vientiane, laid out by the French and the colonial capital of Laos, had broad avenues lined with huge teak and acacia trees. But when we arrived the monsoon rains had turned these unpaved boulevards into rivers of mud, crowded with ancient automobiles, oxcarts, pedestrians, wandering buffalo, and sleepy dogs. Signs of the ending of the French colonial period were everywhere. Paint peeled from buildings in huge patches, there were buffalo wallows on the lawns of the National Assembly, and the caretaker's wife had hung out her laundry along the elaborate colonnades.

That night the boys and I went sight-seeing. Strolling through the city, we found a Laotian "love-court" going on and squatted down in the audience. I had often heard of the unique Lao entertainment which chants of the art of courtship. It is sheer poetry, improvised on the spot. The boy extols the beauty, grace, virtue of the courted maiden; the girl sings of the boy's nobility, charm, bravery.

But I had something else in mind. We needed an interpreter. Baker and I both spoke French fluently, and Pete and Denny had a working knowledge of it. What I wanted was a dependable man or boy who understood the Laotian dialects and could translate into French. Squatting in the love-court audience, I decided to begin the search then and there.

"What is this performance?" I asked loudly in French. "What is the meaning of these words and gestures?"

The people turned and stared at me. Then a voice said: "*Moi parler français, monsieur.*" He introduced himself as Chai, and proceeded to interpret the love poetry into passable French.

Chai was a short, husky lad with beautifully modeled features, wide-set eyes, clear bronze skin, and jet-black hair. He wore the native sarong, knotted at the waist, an immaculate white shirt with French cuffs (the colonial influence), and, of course, no shoes. I remember noticing his short, stubby fingers. I didn't realize that they would one day serve me expertly across the surgical table.

Chai was a graduate of the Vientiane *lycée*, and apparently had a natural flair for languages. I explained that I was a doctor, and that we were going to Vang Vieng (about one hundred and twenty miles north of the capital). When I said we needed an interpreter, he accepted the job enthusiastically. He claimed to know all about Vang Vieng where he had *parentage*—which we would call kinfolk or kissin' cousins.

The setting for Vang Vieng must have been selected by a master artist. It is spectacular. The village rests at the foot of stupendous walls of rock, rising two thousand and three thousand feet into the sky. These mountains have no foothills. There's no gradual rise or slope. Just an absolutely flat plain; then suddenly, abruptly, a staggering wall of rock. The tops of these mountains are covered with pine and on the side walls stubby trees grow out of the rock at painful angles and reach upward for light. The tributary of the Mekong River winds around the mountains in search of lowlands. There are many stories of this river's perils, stories of deadly leeches, parasites, huge fish, rays and snakes, as well as Chai's stories of spirits and dragons.

Thanks chiefly to one elderly member of Chai's *parentage*, whom the boys irreverently named Ojisan (Japanese for "old man"), about half the people of Vang Vieng were out to meet us when the trucks and jeeps of Operation Laos arrived in town. Ojisan had spread the word that we were white medicine men bringing powerful remedies to the people. Hence many of the women and children came with gifts of flowers, cucumbers, and oranges.

We found the Lao dispensary at one end of the square (actually the area surrounding the town well) directly across from the home of the chao muong or mayor. It was a low, whitewashed building of three rooms. Since it had no living quarters, Ojisan gave us a house which he owned at the southern end of the town.

Norman Baker was our chief construction man, in the best Sea-bee tradition; and under his direction the boys went to work converting the dispensary into a small hospital. They swept, swabbed, disinfected, and then whitewashed. With the aid of a half-dozen coolies, we cleared the surrounding yard (which was to serve as our "reception room") of debris, cow dung, and heaps of foul bandages and dressings. Then we built a fence to keep out the wandering water buffalo.

The medical supplies were uncrated, and the boys did an ingenious job of converting the empty boxes into tables and benches, and cabinets in which to store our pharmaceuticals. Then we borrowed some cots from the local detachment of the Royal Lao Army. When these had been deloused and repaired, we set them up in one room which was to serve as the ward.

Our living quarters presented a tougher problem. Ojisan's house was a typical Lao hut perched six feet above ground on stout poles surrounded by a "porch" and reached by a steep ladder. We climbed up, took one look inside, and came out shuddering. The place was filthy.

The boys tore out everything inside the hut including the bamboo partition between the two rooms. They swept the ceiling clear of soot, cobwebs, and rats' nests, then went to work on the walls. When this accumulation of ancient dirt had been swept out, they hauled up buckets of river water, broke out boxes of soap powder and bleach, and swabbed the deck Navy style.

We never announced sick call, and we needed no publicity. Only a few days after our arrival we were awakened one morning by sounds that were to become a familiar part of every dawn—the howls of sickly babies, the hacking coughs of tubercular mothers. Why wait on line at the hospital, when you can camp on the doctor's front porch!

Frankly, I was overwhelmed by the horrible health conditions we found in Vang Vieng. These were yaws, tuberculosis, pneumonia, malaria, and diseases far more heartrending. I was appalled by the sight of so many women mutilated and crippled in childbirth, and by the many traumatic injuries long neglected and horribly infected.

The hideous yaws we could cure with the "1-2-3 treatment"— one shot of penicillin, two bars of soap, and three days! There was little we could do about the tuberculosis, except to control the paroxysms of coughing with cough syrup; for it is the racking cough that frequently causes pneumonia and hastens the tubercular's death.

One of the most horrible diseases for us to treat was leprosy. Here the patients who gaped at us were just remnants of human beings, rotted and bloated beyond ordinary shape. In dealing with this loathsome disease I had constantly to suppress the strong urge of nausea.

More than 50 per cent of the patients we saw had malaria. Usually these people had survived many attacks of the disease, and achieved a certain immunity; but they were left with greatly enlarged spleens. When the spleen is diseased, the blood loses some of its ability to coagulate, and the slightest cut or bruise can cause a serious hemorrhage. So we pumped vitamins into almost every patient we saw.

One morning at sick call a poor woman pushed a huge, smelly bundle of rags into my arms. I peeled away the layers of clothing and uncovered a baby about a year old. It was a hideous sight. The abdomen looked like an overblown balloon that was about to burst, the chest looked like a miniature birdcage. There was a tiny monkey face with wild, unseeing eyes. Kwashiorkor's disease! And this was only the first of countless cases we were to encounter in Laos.

Kwashiorkor's disease, fairly common among backward people in the tropics, is not caused by infection but by ignorance. It is the grotesque result of malnutrition. Metabolism fails, muscles waste away, liver and spleen are enlarged, the abdomen swells, and the heart and circulation are damaged. The end result is death.

But this horrible process is reversible if caught in time. This was an extreme case. The mother had fallen ill and was unable to nurse her baby; so, from the age of about six months, the child was fed only rice and water.

Successful treatment of Kwashiorkor's disease depends upon extremely cautious feeding so as not to overtax the weakened system. We injected vitamins, and then used the wonderful protein powder called MPF (MultiPurpose Food) supplied to us by Meals for Millions. MPF can be used in many ways. Two ounces of the powder made into a broth, for example, provide proteins equivalent to a steak dinner.

We put the baby on a diet of MPF solution and fruit juices and got remarkable results. The damage to the heart and eyes, unfortunately, was irreversible. But the child lived.

That night I told the boys that we were adding another project to our overloaded schedule. We were starting regular classes, open to all comers, in nutrition, hygiene, and similar matters. There was entirely too much disease caused by ignorance in "our town." We might as well get after it now.

Every day, from dawn to high noon, we held sick call at the hospital. In the afternoons we loaded our faithful jeep Agnes and held "jeep call" in the surrounding countryside, often with Pete and Denny in charge when I was doing surgery. Then, in the evenings, the crowds would gather in front of our house for Walt Disney movies—and for our lectures on the facts of living, delivered via our proud interpreter, Chai.

Sick call was always an ordeal; for, aside from disease and ignorance, we had to contend with the quaint customs of the people. The line would form sometimes double in the crowded courtyard and file into the dispensary. I would sit on a chair, with Chai beside me, and try to get the patient to sit on the bench facing me. That wasn't so easy as it sounds.

To the people, the American doctor was a "mandarin"—high on the social totem pole. (Even Chai acquired a certain nobility by association and was always addressed as *Thanh*, an honorific reserved for more important personages.) But the trouble was that, according to long-established custom, the humble Laotian's head could never be higher than the mandarin's. Consequently, when examining a patient, I was forced to bend or squat lower and lower. Sometimes I had to grovel on the dirt floor in order to listen to a heartbeat!

We also had difficulty with the Lao nurses we were trying to train. These earnest, intelligent boys and girls would perform the most distasteful duties, handle any part of a filthy and diseased body. But at first we could not get them to clean a head wound, or even hold a patient's head while I stitched the scalp or pulled a tooth. The Laos believe that the spirit of Buddha resides in the head, hence even touching it is like defiling the tabernacle.

Obstetrics, if I may call it that, was our biggest problem from the outset. We estimated that about 50 per cent of the babies were lost before or during delivery. One out of every five mothers died in childbirth, and many of those who survived were left horribly mutilated.

To the Laotian midwife, the job is over once the baby is born. The child is wrapped and placed in a basket, ashes are rubbed on its forehead, and the grandfather blows into the infant's ear to impart wisdom. Meanwhile, the mother, who has given birth to her baby squatting upright on a stool, lies neglected and often hemorrhaging critically.

Hence, we gave high priority to our midwife training program. There were about four practicing midwives in Vang Vieng when we arrived, and perhaps as many more young girls who aspired to the calling. We won them over to our side, had them help around the hospital, and made them promise to call us for each childbirth. When we went on a call, we would take along one or two of the younger girls. And always we carried a bag containing the wonderful midwife's kit prepared and distributed by CARE. Each of these kits contains gowns, gloves, cord ties, basins, bowls, dressings, soaps, towels, etc.—all the essentials for the delivery of twenty-five babies.

We taught the girls the principles of modern aseptic midwifery. Then, after each one had delivered twenty-five babies under supervision, and had proved her proficiency and dedication, she was "graduated" with appropriate ceremony, climaxed by the presentation of the CARE kit—always the bag that I personally had carried and used. (This was extremely important for "face.")

Just as in America nurses are "capped" at graduation, we "bagged" our midwives in Vang Vieng. And it worked. Those wonderful young women, armed with their CARE kits and somewhat dedicated to the aseptic principles we taught them, have removed many of the old horrors from maternity in that part of Laos.

Our practice of medicine was not confined to humans alone. One day a man came to Pete and presented the symptomatology of his friend. This friend lacked pep, was unable to hold his head up, had bad feet, and was losing weight. The man said that this syndrome came upon the friend a few weeks after he had been badly mauled by a tiger. Peter registered astonishment and in-

quired further, "How old is your friend?" The man had no idea.
Nor could you ask how much weight he had lost, because in
Laos there is no system of measurements for anything of this
size. Peter asked many more questions and finally said that the
man would have to bring his friend to the clinic. The man said that
he had done this already; his friend was tied up outside the hospital. Peter went outside and found the friend, a small Tibetan
pony, tethered to a tree. Pete called to me and I went and joined
in the consultation. Indeed, the pony was in bad shape. The tiger
had torn the throat and chest considerably and had slashed the
forehead open. Each claw mark was infested with maggots. I sent
for water, soap, and cotton, and proceeded to wash and clean
the sores. We put some antiseptic over the wounds and then
wrapped a large dressing around the horse's neck to prevent
further maggot infestation. Pete rotated around each end of the
horse injecting penicillin, none of us knowing the exact dosage of
the antibiotic for horses. This patient came back every day
looking a little better each time. Finally we discharged him from
the active-treatment list. It was now too late to save ourselves; the
word spread, and hardly a week passed that someone did not
bring a horse or a water buffalo to us for treatment. The com-
plaints were as myriad as those of the two-legged patients—bad
eyes, cough, loss of weight, fever, or just senility.

One dawn we were sitting around our not-yet-completed
house eating C rations and coffee for breakfast. I glanced at the
gathering of women on the front porch and was commenting to
Pete about it. There were usually people there every morning,
but this day there were so many they had overflowed to the front
lawn. Among them was a small young lad of about twelve years
old, who was not a member of the Lao race but rather was a
Kha tribesman. All of the people looked bad, but this lad looked
worse than any. He was squatting, shivering in the early-morning
coolness, draped in filthy rags. When I left the house to walk

down the lane to the hospital, he got off his haunches and said, "*Koi chep ken kenoi,*" which means, "I have a sore leg."

When I looked at the massive infection from an old cut on his leg, I wondered how on earth he could even walk. I asked him through Chai, the interpreter, how he had come to us. He said he had walked two days and two nights and had arrived at our house around midnight last night. Why did a feverish lad spend a cold and dismal night squatting outside my house? "I did not think it would be right to disturb the American mandarins while they slept."

We started immediate treatment. Under anesthesia we slashed open the pus pockets of his leg and drained them. We gave him penicillin and antipyretics. We did not put on any dressings but let him lie in bed on clean sheets, allowing the pus to drain out of the open tracts. Several days later we convinced him of the attractiveness and the importance of a bath in the river, which was just down the road a bit. Even with his fever, a bath was imperative.

We gave him soap and a brush and he hobbled on down and scrubbed like he had never scrubbed before in his life. He wanted to please us. My boys rewarded him by giving him one of their clean T-shirts and a pair of khaki pants, and they then gave him a fine new CARE blanket that he could keep. The Kha boy was overwhelmed. Rarely have I seen a happier boy. He spent the next ten days in our new hospital receiving antibiotics, vitamins, and what American nurses call "T.L.C.," tender, loving care. This is what he devoured more than anything. He liked being liked. He loved being cared for. This wistful lad had suffered a lot and deserved some happiness. He had the right to disturb us whenever he wanted to. We explained this to him repeatedly. When we discharged him he was cured of the staphyloccus infection of his leg, and cured of the more insidious poison, fear.

Never in the thousands of hours that I had devoted to thinking about and planning for this mission in Laos did I anticipate the depths of misery in which we would have to work and eat and sleep and live. Never did anybody in the Washington briefings, in the Laotian Embassy, or in the refugee camps of Vietnam adequately indicate what life would be like for us four Americans in the tropical jungles of Central Laos. I was completely stunned by the conditions that existed in the village of Vang Vieng.

As the weeks progressed we became more renowned throughout the area. We always urged the villagers to pay us in barter for our medicines and for the treatment that we were giving. This was important for their own pride and was important for us, too. It was expensive running this mission, and the simple idea of having our patients pay us in produce assumed great importance. At the end of a day in the clinic we would have a dozen eggs, several coconuts, and, if the day was good, a scrawny chicken.

A jeep call consisted of two members of the team driving to one of the dozens of outlying villages around Vang Vieng. The jeep would be driven into the village with the horn blaring. We would park, drop the tailgate, send someone for a bucket of water, and open the boxes of medicines. At once our portable clinic would be plunged into its flourishing practice. The people we would care for in the afternoons were those who were either too sick or not sick enough to make it to Vang Vieng, perhaps a four-hour walk away.

On jeep call there was not the nerve-racking pressure of misery and confinement that we felt in the crowded room at the clinic. At least we had mobility and a measure of fresh air. We knew the importance of going into the huts of these people. Never had they seen an American. Never had they received white men in their homes, and they were just as proud of their homes as we are. I would estimate that we have been in more than three thousand Asian homes. Often the insides of these huts were op-

pressively sultry and humid, most of them by our standards were
filthy, and they were plagued with lice, fleas, gnats, and insects.
Always in the darkest corners there were the potbellied children,
the undernourished, the malnourished, and the miserable.

We always carried a black bag, a must for M.D.'s in America
and a good idea in Laos, too. In the jeep we would bring extra
boxes of combiotic, terramycin, Meals for Millions, sterile solutions, T-shirts, and perhaps some candy as distractions and bribes
for the young and old.

Every couple of weeks two members of my team would take
the drive through the jungle to get to Vientiane. They would
pick up the mail, send ours out, buy whatever supplies were
needed, load all into the trailer, and return the next day to Vang
Vieng. Every month we would have to buy another barrel of
gasoline and gingerly carry it to our village on the tired back of
Agnes.

Though it was always a break to get away from the clinic, the
jeep drive was a frightening experience. If the vehicle should
break down, it was certain that the two men would have to hike
for several days in order to get to the capital. There was rarely
any traffic on the road during these months. In spite of Baker's
administerings, Agnes was limping and lugging herself around,
showing the result of her arduous and frequent jeep calls.

I cannot give full praise to these men of mine. They did the
dirty work, seldom grumbling and usually joking a bit. They
were excellent men in every sense of the word. Peter Kessey had
a willing heart and a gentle hand; he spoke to the people in a
Texas-American accent, and somehow they always seemed to
understand. Norman Baker, my French-speaking mechanic and
general man around the place, could slap on a dressing that was
guaranteed never to come off; he would sweat and grunt but he
got it on and it stayed on. Denny Shepard, who was going on to
medical school, was brilliant and practiced a high caliber of
medicine. I am afraid Dooley was a hard taskmaster; I frequently

lost my temper, but the boys persisted. I believe that my men showed heroism, sacrifice, and guts, not in any one great dramatic action, but rather in constancy.

We kept a twenty-dollar bill tacked on the wall. The understanding was that anyone who got mad, or homesick, or just fed up with the job could take it and head for home. No one ever touched that money. But I am sure there were many times when the boys were tempted during those endless days and nights of dealing with misery, filth, and disease.

Denny, the newlywed, missed his wife terribly, and spent his odd moments composing lengthy letters. Norman Baker became increasingly jittery as the time for the baby's arrival drew near. (Fortunately, my mother kept in close touch with Priscilla; and when Master Arthur Thomas Baker showed up one day in November the excited father got the good news in less than seventy-two hours, thanks to the embassy mailroom in Vientiane!)

One day in November we were busy as usual, and at midday we just bolted our food and went back to work. While nobody mentioned it, we were all aware that the day was Thanksgiving. We were just a little more homesick than usual. Then, along toward dusk, we heard the roar of a jeep. A cloud of dust boiled up the road to our house and out stepped a short, chubby young man with a wonderful smile—Jefferson Davis Cheek of Comanche, Texas.

Jeff Cheek, who was attached to the USOM in Vientiane, was one of our few and infrequent visitors. Now he announced that he was dirty, tired, and hungry after the long trek from Vientiane. He demanded to know what we had to eat.

"C rations, brother!" said Pete. "Today it's beef and peas plus rice." Jeff laughed and hauled a dusty bag out of the back of his jeep. It contained a complete Thanksgiving dinner—roast turkey, cranberry sauce, mashed potatoes, pumpkin pie. He had even brought along the alcoholic trimmings, which we enjoyed while the food was heating in the hospital sterilizer.

After we had feasted royally, we sat out on the porch and talked about Savong, the little girl Jeff once had brought to us from Ban Tsieng.

We had been in Vang Vieng only a few weeks when Jeff Cheek came to visit us for the first time. He was driving along the jungle trail when a group of natives stopped his jeep and appealed for help. They showed him a little girl, about fourteen years old, lying on a mat, semiconscious and obviously near death.

This was Savong. Some time earlier, no one knew how long ago, she had scratched her leg in the jungle and it became infected. Ignorant and helpless, Savong's people just left her lying in the hut. Eventually the entire leg became horribly bloated and the infection spread up into the groin. That was the way Jeff found her.

He placed her gently in the back of the jeep, and drove slowly through the jungle, reaching Vang Vieng after dark. We opened up the hospital, but after one look I had my doubts about saving her. Yet there was something about this child that touched us deeply. She seemed symbolic of all the miserable, neglected kids in Laos—Southeast Asia is full of Savongs. So we were determined to save her.

Of course she was filthy after such long neglect. We literally had to scrub the nearly lifeless little body with soap and brush before proceeding. Then, when she was clean, we gave her a minimum of anesthesia, and I began to operate.

I had to incise the bloated leg from knee to groin. The horrible green pus filled several containers. When the drainage stopped, I saw the cellulitis, which can best be described as a mass of boils involving the muscles and underlying tissues. When we got through, there was nothing left of that massive leg but bone and a few soggy muscles.

She had lain for so many months in one position that her

"good" side was covered with massive, weeping pressure sores which we cleaned and dressed. Then we revived her and administered infusions of saline and glucose.

Pete, Denny, Baker, and even Chai took turns hovering over Savong all through that night and the next day. The fever dropped, she brightened, and then began to cry. Not from pain now, but because her anguish was over. Between sobs we heard her mumbling *"Cop chai, cop chai, cop chai. . . ."* Over and over—"Thank you, thank you, thank you. . . ."

Weeks passed, and Savong grew stronger. First she sat up, then she walked a few steps. The boys trimmed her hair in a sort of feather bob, gave her a toothbrush and taught her how to use it. Somehow they even obtained female clothes. Then Jeff Cheek came with presents of hair ribbons and combs. We decided that Savong really looked beautiful.

Months later we discharged her. She was strong and well, although she limped a bit on that frail little leg. Her people came to take her back to Ban Tsieng.

Before she left we took a picture of her. We gave one print to Jeff Cheek because, we said teasingly, Savong was "his girl." The other print we kept for ourselves. Whenever we felt homesick or disheartened we would look at that picture of Savong. It served to remind us that, for some people, things might have been different had we stayed comfortably at home.

Toward dusk one evening, early in December, I watched the crowd gather in front of our house for movies.

When the picture began I took my favorite seat on the porch, above and behind the screen. From there I could study these wonderful faces, young and old, glowing in the light reflected from the screen.

I thought: How many times had I been told that the Laos were lazy people, ignorant, backward, indifferent to their own betterment? How many times has that canard been uttered by cynical Westerners against neglected people everywhere who never had a chance? Here in Vang Vieng I had living proof of its falsity. Never have I seen people respond so readily to encouragement, or to make so much from so little help.

Our classes in sanitation, hygiene, food and nutrition, infant and child care were popular and paying off handsomely. We had "bagged" many midwives, and these girls had achieved an *esprit de corps* that had elevated midwifery to a proud profession that attracted other candidates. The Lao nurses were increasing in number and proficiency. Each fortnight, by arrangement, when the boys made the trip to Vientiane for mail and supplies, they brought back a senior from the *lycée* for a week. We hoped to inspire these young men to study medicine. Already we had trained a dozen "practical" nurses, more than were needed in Vang Vieng.

Now, I knew, the time was approaching when we would have to "phase out" of Vang Vieng. My mission was not to set up a permanent American outpost, but to establish something that the Laos themselves could carry on. True, it would be primitive by Western standards, but it would be better than what these people had before.

Kam Lak, the senior nurse, would take charge. He was a conscientious, highly intelligent young man who already could be entrusted with minor surgery. Kam Ba, his wife, who was probably the best of our midwives, could serve as his assistant. We left them a few surgical instruments and about $10,000 worth of drugs. The Ministry promised them further supplies.

Now I faced the difficult task of "closing out" of Vang Vieng.

We held our last class in the local school and asked the children to remember what we had taught them. They replied that they would not forget their Americans. We graduated and "bagged" some more girls from the midwife training course, and began to plan our days in January.

We were timing this phase out. We did not wish to offend the village by leaving abruptly so we planned to spend four or five weeks doing our work as usual, explaining to each day's sick call that we would soon be leaving and that the Lao nurse and mid-wives would continue our work. We told all the villages that these people were very capable and that we would leave the white man's miraculous medicines behind for the villagers. They were sad to see us go but pleased that we were leaving things behind.

The town of Vang Vieng gave us an elaborate *baci*, a ritualistic ceremony, climaxed by a grand feast, which the Laos hold to celebrate a birth, a marriage, a soldier's return from the wars, or the departure of cherished friends. The women of the village built a small pyramid from palm leaves, and decorated it with flowers, candles, baubles, and bangles. The finished product stood about two feet high. It was then placed in a beautiful hand-made silver bowl. From the top of the pyramid to the bottom of the bowl long streamers of white cotton were hung. Around the base of the bowl the women placed, with great precision, succulent pieces of pork, rice, sweetmeats, and other delicacies.

All the participants in the *baci* then sat in a large circle on new mats or blankets around the center pyramid of flowers, close enough to lean forward and touch the bowl with an outstretched hand.

An old sorcerer then chanted the Invocation to the Spirits. We sat on the floor with our long legs tucked beside us, our left hand held up as if in prayer, and our right palm extended upward touching the bowl. He begged all the divinities of Dawn and Dusk, the spirits of Night and Day, and the nymphs of the Mountains and Flowers to come to this *baci* and partake of the food which is laid out for them.

After the sorcerer felt that all the spirits were present, he called on the souls of those for whom the *baci* was being given. The Lao tribes feel that the soul is a vagabond, and must be recalled to the body from time to time. The second part of the *baci* then began.

The sorcerer first took a piece of cotton string from the center pyramid of blossoms and knelt in front of those for whom the *baci* was being offered. He made a wish for me, and while chanting his wish he tied a string around my wrist, and very meticulously twirled the ends lest the wish fall out of the string. When he finished with me, a second person tied another cotton on my wrist, and a third, and so on. This was repeated for each of us. By the time the ceremony was finished, we had more than a dozen cotton strings around our wrists. Each offered a wish, and each was a bit more bizarre than the former:

"May you always be strong against the tusks of elephants."

"May you be safe from the jaws of the wild boar."

"May you be rich."

"May you have many wives."

"May you possess all wisdom and health."

"May you be blessed with prosperity and strength."

"May your jeep not fall off the road nor your airplane from the sky."

"May you always carry with you our love."

"May you return to us, your friends."

The old beetle-chewing women, the wise elders of the village, the giggling girls, the mayor, all tied on us the cotton strings of friendship and called on the presiding spirits to witness the sincerity of their wishes.

Chai had told us that the person receiving the *baci*, to show his gratitude and understanding, must do his part. So after each string was tied, we clasped our hands together in praying attitude, and said, "*Cop chai liiiiii, saaaa.*"

After the *baci* was finished, the sorcerer again thanked the spirits and told them they might leave, and the souls that they might return to their life of roaming. Then everyone started to eat the rice balls, sweetmeats, and the other food that the spirits didn't eat.

Finally the day came for our leaving. We had everything crated up and were sitting on the front porch of our now-empty house. The army trucks that the minister was sending up to us were due in an hour.

Hundreds of people had gathered in the square to bid us farewell. We had *baci* strings tied around our wrists almost up to the elbow. The villagers brought many going-away gifts—flowers, corn, chicken, gifts of good wishes. We said many farewells to Ojisan, the nurse, the mayor, the kids.

The last glimpse we had of the villagers of Vang Vieng was from the back of an army truck as it jolted along toward the jungle road. They looked like a lot of little bears, pawing the air as they waved their arms *toward themselves* in the parting gesture that means "come back soon."

A Man from Mexico

by Berton Roueché

Medical science continues its fight against disease with new vaccines and new antibiotics, for which the great drug houses scour the earth and will no doubt someday sample other planets. Yet eternal vigilance remains the price of public health.

That is the moral of the medical thriller "A Man from Mexico." As early as 1798 Edward Jenner made the first great discovery in vaccination, when he learned how to prevent smallpox. News of this method was rapidly carried to the ends of the earth. The Dowager Empress of Russia and savage tribes of American Indians were alike in paying him honor. So successful was his technique that many modern physicians have felt that smallpox is an anachronism. Roueché shows how close we can still come to the edge of destruction and how valuable such organizations as local and national departments of health can be.

Smallpox is an ancient and immoderately ferocious disease of oriental origin that shares with plague, cholera, and epidemic typhus the distinction of having once or twice in the past five hundred years come fairly close to eradicating the human race. It is less unmanageable now. A full-fledged smallpox epidemic has been nearly unheard of since the late nineteenth century. Except in a few parts of the world—most of them easygoing—the appearance of even a handful of cases is an unusual occurrence. The only countries in which serious outbreaks have been at all frequent in recent years are India, Japan, Siam, Korea, British East Africa, Venezuela, and the United States.

About the best that can be said for smallpox is that it is somewhat less barbaric than plague. Plague is almost invariably fatal. Smallpox strikes with varying degrees of intensity, and in some epidemics there have been so many mild cases that a large majority of the victims have recovered, but the disease is by no means always so benign. At its worst—when it is known as black, or hemorrhagic, smallpox—it is almost always lethal. Victims of even the blandest attacks of smallpox occasionally succumb to one or another of several complications to which the disease is hospitable, among them septic poisoning and broncho pneumonia, and those fortunate enough to survive an attack are often crippled for life. Blindness is a possible, though uncommon, consequence. Few have ever emerged scot-free from an attack of smallpox. Because of the pustular eruptions that characterize the disease, and from which its name is derived, it is almost certain to be permanently disfiguring. It can also be one of the most unnerving and repulsive of ailments. "The patient often becomes a dripping, unrecognizable mass of pus by the seventh or eighth day of eruption," Dr. Archibald L. Hoyne, medical superintendent of the Chicago Municipal Contagious Disease Hospital, has noted in a clinical study. "The putrid odor is stifling, the temperature often high [107° has been authoritatively reported], and the patient frequently in a wild state of delirium." Moreover, unlike plague, cholera, typhus, and many other deadly infections, the transmission of which is usually limited to either a carrier insect or contaminated drinking water, smallpox is abundantly contagious. Some epidemiologists consider it the most contagious of all diseases, including measles and the common cold.

The cause of smallpox is a durable virus. It enters the body through the respiratory system and is present in the exhalations of its victims for hours, and very likely days, before the apparent onset of illness. It is prolifically communicable during the entire course of the disease and may even be contracted from a victim some hours after his death. It can be conveyed by clothing, books, or letters, and there is good reason to believe that it is as readily air-borne as dust. Nobody is naturally immune to smallpox, survival of one attack is no absolute assurance of future immunity, and, since both nonagenarians and unborn babies have been stricken, susceptibility is seemingly unrelated to age. A specific cure has yet to be discovered, and medical treatment, while desirable, is merely palliative. However, smallpox is not unavoidable. It is, in fact, among the few diseases against which certain immunization is possible. "There is no more certain truth in all the world," Dr. Hoyne has written, "than that an individual properly vaccinated with potent lymph [living virus] cannot contract smallpox in any manner whatsoever."

Many physicians are inclined these days to regard smallpox as an anachronism. This assumption, though infirm, is by no means unreasonable. The development of a reliable method of preventing the disease is not only one of scientific medicine's loftiest triumphs but one of its earliest; by illuminating the mechanics of disease in general, vaccination, which dates from the eighteenth century, inspired the immunological discoveries of Pasteur, Von Behring, Ehrlich, and others. Long before the discovery of vaccination, it was possible to exert some preventive control over smallpox. In the third century before Christ pioneering healers in India became aware that the injection of a minute quantity of virulent smallpox matter into a healthy person often produced a painless seizure and subsequent immunity. Inoculation, as this procedure came to be known, was introduced into Europe, by way of Turkey, in 1717, or thereabouts, and was widely practiced on the Continent and elsewhere until vaccination turned up a couple of generations later. The first deliberate vaccination was performed by an English dairy farmer named Benjamin Jesty in

1774. Jesty had observed that milkmaids who had suffered an attack of vaccinia, or cowpox—a harmless occupational malaise of bovine derivation—seemed to be impervious to smallpox. He conceived the useful notion of relating that barnyard phenomenon to the technique of inoculation, and, using lymph from an ailing cow, immunized himself and his wife and children, at least to his own satisfaction. As a vaccinator, Jesty apparently confined his efforts to the family circle. It is possible that Dr. Edward Jenner, a British physician who is more commonly celebrated as the discoverer of vaccination, never heard of him. Dr. Jenner vaccinated his first patient in 1796, with the same sort of lymph Jesty had employed. Two years later he published his revolutionary treatise "An Inquiry into the Causes and Effects of the Variolæ Vaccinæ, a Disease Discovered in Some of the Western Counties of England, Particularly Gloucestershire, and Known by the Name of the Cowpox." Inoculation has two drawbacks as a smallpox preventive. In addition to being uncomfortably speculative, the seizure it brings on is as contagious as the real thing. Since the virus of cowpox, though the disease is probably a form of smallpox, is consistently effective but innocuous, vaccination has neither of these imperfections. Its only flaw, an easily remedied one, is that the immunity conferred by it diminishes with the passage of time.

The model efficiency of vaccination was almost at once recognized throughout the world. The first American vaccinator, Dr. Benjamin Waterhouse, professor of physics at the Harvard University Medical School, immunized his first patient in 1800. Not long after, in England, the Bishop of Worcester set a clerical precedent by commending the practice to his communicants. In 1805 Napoleon made vaccination compulsory in the French Army, a precaution that has since been taken by the military authorities of nearly all nations, and persuasively urged it upon civilians, not only in France but in Italy as well. Compulsory

vaccination of everybody was presently instituted in many countries—Bavaria (1807), Norway, Denmark, and Iceland (1810),
Sweden (1814), the German states (1818), Great Britain (1853),
Rumania (1874), Hungary (1876), and Austria (1886). Other
countries have since become equally thorough, but the United
States is not among them. Compulsory vaccination has always
been considered unnecessary here, except for the armed forces. In
some states and in some cities (New York City is one) it is required only as a prerequisite to attending elementary school. Even
this gentle bit of coercion has occasionally been opposed by pa-
triots as tyrannical.

In the spring of 1947, to the unnatural astonishment of the press,
the public, and most physicians, smallpox reappeared, after an
absence of not quite eight years, in New York City. It struck,
altogether, twelve men, women, and children. Two of them died.
Largely because of dazzling good luck and the dispatch with
which the Department of Health tracked down and sequestered
several hundred people presumed to have been exposed to the disease, the outbreak proved to be one of the mildest on record. It
could have been hair-raising. Dr. Morris Greenberg, director of
the Department's Bureau of Preventable Diseases, has estimated
that at the time the first victim died only about two million of
the city's nearly eight million inhabitants had any degree of
immunity whatever to smallpox.

The New York City Health Department, to which the appearance of a serious communicable disease anywhere in the city
must be promptly reported, learned of the 1947 outbreak toward
noon on Friday, March 28. Its informant was Dr. Dorothea M.
Tolle, medical superintendent of Willard Parker Hospital, a
municipal institution for the treatment of contagious diseases, at
the foot of East Fifteenth Street.* Her report which she made by
telephone, as is customary when a potentially fast-moving con-

* Willard Parker Hospital was closed on December 1, 1955.

tagion is involved, was inconclusive but disheartening. Two patients, whose trouble was at first believed to be chicken pox, had overnight developed eruptions that looked alarmingly like those of smallpox. Dr. Edward M. Bernecker, commissioner of hospitals, and Dr. Ralph S. Muckenfuss, director of the Bureau of Laboratories, had both been apprised of the occurrence, she added, and the latter was arranging for a definitive laboratory analysis of material taken from the patients. Dr. Tolle's lack of certainty, which was shared by her deputy, Dr. Irving Klein, and the other members of the Willard Parker staff, was not surprising. Smallpox has always been an elusive disease to diagnose in its early stages, the symptoms that mark its onset—chills, fever, headache, and nausea—being indistinguishable from those of influenza, malaria, and typhoid fever. Bedside recognition of it at any stage is difficult now, for contemporary physicians generally find even the rash peculiar to the disease—a rash that emerges on the third or fourth day of illness and becomes pustular by the eighth—more confusing than enlightening. One reason for this diagnostic stumbling is that many doctors currently in practice have never seen a case of smallpox. Another is that several other rashy disorders —among them chicken pox, measles, scarlet fever, scabies, acne, impetigo, syphilis, and ulcerative endocarditis—are more insistently prevalent and, consequently, come more readily to mind. The thought of smallpox forced itself upon Dr. Tolle and Dr. Klein that Friday morning in 1947 mainly because the rash displayed by the two invalids was, providentially, of an almost classic clarity.

By one o'clock copies of Dr. Tolle's report had been distributed to all administrative officers of the Department and an investigation of the cases was briskly under way. Its pattern, despite the unusual nature of the alarm, was routine and confidential. As a preliminary defensive measure, Dr. Bernecker and Dr. Israel Weinstein, then commissioner of health, ordered a speedy vaccination of everybody at Willard Parker—doctors, nurses, lay employees, and patients—and instructed the authorities there not to admit any visitor who declined to be vaccinated on the spot. A summary clinical inquiry was at the same time, and as a matter of course, undertaken by Dr. David A. Singer, chief diagnostician of the Manhattan division of the Bureau of Preventable Diseases. He lit out for the hospital the moment the notification reached him. He found both suspected victims flushed, feverish, freshly vaccinated, and tucked away in individual, glassed-in cubicles in a remote corner of an isolation building. One of them was a twenty-six-year-old Puerto Rican, who, because of the turn events took in his instance, can be specifically identified as Ismael Acosta. The other was a Negro infant, Patricia G——, aged twenty-two months, whose name, like the names of most patients under such circumstances, can be given only in part. Dr. Singer's diagnosis, which he presently telephoned to Dr. Greenberg, his superior, tentatively confirmed the suspicions of Dr. Tolle and Dr. Klein. Dr. Muckenfuss, meanwhile, within an hour after being alerted by Dr. Tolle, had obtained some fluid from the lesions of the two patients and dispatched the samples by plane to Dr. Joseph Smadel, director of the United States Army Medical School Laboratory, in Washington, for full-scale examination. His choice of the Army Laboratory was instinctive; at the time it was the closest to New York of the few laboratories in the country that were equipped to perform the intricate and time-consuming tests by which the presence of smallpox virus can be detected. Then, before turning his attention to other things, Dr. Muckenfuss got in touch with Dr. Weinstein. He told him that a dependable yes-or-no answer from Dr. Smadel should be along in about a week.

The cheerless uniformity of the clinical opinions of Dr. Tolle, Dr. Klein, and Dr. Singer gave Dr. Weinstein little reason to hope for a relaxing word from Dr. Smadel, but he felt restrained by the lack of absolute certainty from authorizing at the moment a far-reaching investigation. He preferred, so long as there was any doubt, to shield the city from the shrieks and speculations of the press. His discretion did not, however, encourage departmental idleness. The next morning, Saturday, March 29, as part of the undercover investigation, a couple of the most inquisitive operatives in the Bureau of Preventable Diseases were quietly assigned to assist Dr. Singer. Their job was to discover where and how, if Acosta and Patricia did have smallpox, the disease had been contracted. To this end, with the lively cooperation of Dr. Tolle and Dr. Klein, they fixed their attention on the hospital records. Taken together, the dossiers of the two patients made provocative reading. Acosta was married, lived in the East Bronx, was employed as a porter at Bellevue Hospital, and had reached Willard Parker on Thursday, March 27, having first spent two days in the dermatologic ward at Bellevue. The baby had been admitted to Willard Parker six days before Acosta. She had fallen sick on March 19. Two days later her parents had taken her to a clinic near their home, in Harlem, and from there she had been sent at once to Willard Parker. What quickened the interest of the investigators was that neither of the patients was a newcomer to the hospital. Both had been there previously, and at the same time. Less than a month before Acosta had spent a couple of weeks—from February 27 to March 11—at Willard Parker, with the mumps. Patricia's earlier visit, the outcome of an attack of croup, had lasted from February 28 to March 13. Dr. Singer and his colleagues, mindful that the incubation period of smallpox is generally around twelve to fourteen days and never more than twenty-one, made themselves comfortable and began to absorb this instructive set of coincidences. By Saturday evening they had been led to the somewhat reassuring suspicion that Acosta and Patricia had acquired the disease from the same source. Over the weekend a third and equally probable case of smallpox was uncovered in Willard Parker. The new victim was a boy of two and a half, named John F———, who had been in the hospital, suffering from whooping cough, since March 6. The fact that his had been an uninterrupted confinement strengthened the investigators' hunch to a near certainty. They concluded that Acosta, Patricia, and John had contracted smallpox at the hospital from somebody who had been there between March 6 and March 13.

The unflattering implications of this conclusion embarrassed Dr. Tolle and Dr. Klein, but only momentarily. They calmed themselves with the reflection that diagnostic infallibility is more often the aspiration than the achievement of any hospital staff. To Dr. Klein, the experience was even salutary, and he emerged from it both unruffled and inspired. Memory revived in him with the abruptness of revelation. Early in March, he now recalled, there had been a patient at Willard Parker in whom one physician had fleetingly thought he detected indications of smallpox. Dr. Klein guided the investigators back to the files and, after some digging, produced the record of the patient he had in mind. It was that of a man named Eugene La Bar, and the case it described was morbid, chaotic, and dismaying. La Bar, an American, had lived since 1940 in Mexico City, where he had desultorily engaged in exporting leather goods. He was forty-seven years old, married, and childless. Toward the end of February he and his wife had left Mexico City and headed for New York, traveling by bus. It was their intention to go right on to Readfield, Maine, to view a farm that Mrs. La Bar had just inherited near there, but La Bar became ill during the journey. His discomfort, which he attempted to relieve by frequent doses of aspirin, codeine, Nembutal, and phenobarbital, consisted of a headache and a severe pain in the back of the neck. By the time the couple reached New York, La Bar felt too unwell to go any farther. As far as could be ascertained from the record, he had gone at once to the clinic at Bellevue, where an examining physician, observing that he had a fever of 105° and an odd rash on his face and hands, admitted him to the hospital's dermatologic ward. The date of his admittance was March 5, a Wednesday. Three days later, on March 8, La Bar was transferred to Willard Parker, his condition having baffled and finally frightened the Bellevue dermatologists. He arrived there more dead than alive. The rash by then covered his entire body, and it was pustular and hemorrhagic. It was this rash that prompted one of the Willard Parker doctors to offer a halfhearted diagnosis of smallpox. It also impelled him to vaccinate Mrs. La Bar when she called at the hospital that afternoon to inquire about her husband. Then the physician dropped the theory. His reasons were plausible. A freehand analysis of material taken from the lesions did not appear to support his guess; the rash, upon closer scrutiny, was not strikingly typical of smallpox; La Bar had an old but well-developed vaccination scar; and Mrs. La Bar insisted that her husband could not possibly have been in recent contact with anybody suffering from the disease. Three other diagnoses that had also been more or less seriously considered were enumerated in the record. One, suggested by the vigor and variety of the painkillers with which La Bar had stuffed himself, was drug poisoning. Another was Kaposi's varicelliform eruption, a kind of edema complicated by pustules. The third was erythema multiforme, an acute skin infection, and this had seemed the likeliest. La Bar lay in an agony of delirium for two days. On Monday morning, March 10, his fever suddenly vanished and he felt almost well. Late that afternoon he died. An autopsy disclosed, among other internal dishevelments, an enlarged spleen, a friable liver, and multiple hemorrhages in the viscera and the lungs. The final entry on the record was the cause of death: "Erythema multiforme, with laryngotracheo bronchitis and bronchopneumonia." It was not a deduction in which Dr. Klein and the Health Department physicians, whose wits had been sharpened by hindsight, were tempted to concur. Their persuasion was that they had

just read a forceful account of an unusually virulent attack of
black smallpox.

On the morning of Friday, April 4, the report from Dr. Smadel
came through. It was affirmative: both Acosta and Patricia had
smallpox. (Subsequently, Dr. Smadel was able to say the same of
John and several others, including the deceased La Bar; some
material taken from the latter's lesions for the test made at the
hospital had, it developed, fortunately been preserved.) Dr.
Weinstein received the report without marked consternation. His
reaction was almost one of relief. It delivered him from the misery
of retaining an increasingly unreasonable doubt. It also propelled
him into rapid motion. He notified the United States Public
Health Service of the outbreak. Then he had a word of counsel
with Dr. Bernecker. After that, he assembled the administrative
officers of the Departments of Health and of Hospitals for a
briefing on tactics. Next, waving Dr. Greenberg's agents out into
the open, he set a full-dress investigation in motion. At two
o'clock Dr. Weinstein broke the news to the press at a conference
in his office. His statement included an exhortation. "It is not
surprising that smallpox has reappeared in this city," he said. "The
Health Department has stated many times that we are exposed to
communicable diseases occurring in this and neighboring countries. The danger of a widespread epidemic is slight, because our
population is for the most part protected by vaccination. Smallpox
is one of the most communicable of all diseases, and the only
known preventive measure is vaccination. Anyone in the city who
has never been vaccinated, or who has not been vaccinated since
early childhood, should get this protection at once. Smallpox is a
serious disease that may cause permanent disfigurement, damage
to vital organs, and even death. With vaccination, a simple and
harmless procedure, available to all, there is absolutely no excuse
for anyone to remain unprotected." Dr. Weinstein was aware, as
he spoke, that his advice was somewhat sounder than his optimism.

The public investigation, like the plain-clothes reconnaissance that had preceded it, was accompanied by a quarantine measure; the dermatologic ward at Bellevue was closed to visitors who could not give convincing assurance that they had recently been vaccinated. In addition, vaccination of the entire population of the hospital commenced—a considerable task in itself, which was entrusted to the Department of Hospitals and the Bellevue staff. The rest of the undertaking was handled, without complaint, by the Bureau of Preventable Diseases. It involved the tracking down, the vaccination, and the continued surveillance during the smallpox period of incubation of every person who was known to have been exposed to the disease. Dr. Greenberg's medical staff consists of, in addition to himself and Dr. Singer, three full-time inspectors and thirty-five part-time men. He put them all to work on the task. By nightfall on Friday, less than twelve hours after the arrival of Dr. Smadel's report, Dr. Greenberg's men had called upon, examined, and vaccinated some two hundred potential victims and were on the trail of several hundred others. These two groups comprised all the residents of the apartment buildings in which the Acostas and Patricia's family lived, everyone who had been in the Harlem clinic on the day of Patricia's visit, and everyone who had set foot in Willard Parker between March 8 and March 27 or in the Bellevue dermatologic ward between March 5 and March 8 or between March 25 and March 27, but they did not comprise all those who might conceivably have been infected. This was no reflection on the resourcefulness of the Bureau men. Dr. Weinstein and his associates had known from the outset that the city contained innumerable possible smallpox cases who were beyond the timely reach of any investigators. They were the people among whom La Bar, on March 5, and Patricia, on March 21, and Acosta, on March 25, had passed on their way to the hospital. It was largely Acosta's means of getting there that prompted Dr. Weinstein to try to stimulate in the public an

orderly but general desire for vaccination. La Bar had traveled in
the moderate seclusion of a cab, and Patricia had left the clinic
in an ambulance. Acosta had taken the subway and a crosstown
bus.

The immediate response to Dr. Weinstein's exhortation, which
he quickly condensed for press and radio use into the slogan "Be
Sure, Be Safe, Get Vaccinated!" was only mildly gratifying. Un-
dismayed, he instructed the Bureau of Laboratories at once to set
about converting its bulk supplies of vaccine into handy, one-dose
units and to make these available without charge, through drug-
stores, to all physicians and, directly, to all hospitals and to the
city's twenty-one district health centers. He issued a public statement emphasizing that the protection he recommended was free
as well as simple and harmless. Over the weekend his meaning
appeared to have been caught only by the prudent and the
panicky, but on Monday, April 7, an encouragingly widened
comprehension was perceptible. There was good reason. Two
new cases of suspected smallpox had turned up and been proclaimed. Acosta's wife, who was twenty-six years old and in the
seventh month of pregnancy, was one of them. She had become ill
at her home on Saturday night. The following morning the in-
spector assigned to patrol the building took one alert look at her
and summoned a Willard Parker ambulance. The other was a
Cuban, who, as it later turned out, had nothing worse than
chicken pox, but by the time his case was correctly diagnosed another case of smallpox had come to light. This was on Thursday,
April 10. The patient was a forty-three-year-old wanderer named
Herman G——, whose condition had come to the attention of a
physician in the dermatologic ward at Bellevue, where he had
been confined for treatment since March 10. The next day, April
11, still another victim was reported. He was a businessman of
fifty-seven named Harry T——, and his case, too, was discovered
in the Bellevue dermatologic ward. He had been admitted there,

suffering from lymphoblastoma, on March 19. His misfortune, as the newspapers loudly and uneasily pointed out, brought the number of smallpox cases to seven. It also had the effect of abruptly increasing to around a hundred thousand the number of people who had heeded Dr. Weinstein's admonition.

While dutifully notifying the United States Public Health Service of the outbreak and its transcontinental origin, Dr. Weinstein had expressed a normal interest in Mrs. La Bar's whereabouts and the state of her health. It was his understanding, he said, that she had continued on to Maine soon after her husband's funeral; nothing had been heard from her since, although the true cause of her husband's death had been widely publicized. As might be expected, Dr. Weinstein's curiosity concerning Mrs. La Bar was at least equaled by that of the Public Health Service. He was promised an early reply, and on Wednesday, April 9, his day was enlivened by a report from the Service on its findings. They were numerous and in some respects reassuring, in others highly disturbing. Mrs. La Bar was at the home of a relative in East Winthrop, Maine, and in excellent health. Information obtained from her had enabled the Service to alert the health authorities in the towns at which the La Bars' bus had stopped—Laredo, San Antonio, Dallas, Tulsa, Joplin, St. Louis, Indianapolis, Cincinnati, and Pittsburgh. None had reported any local evidence of smallpox. La Bar's illness apparently hadn't reached a highly contagious stage during the journey. What distressed Dr. Weinstein was the disclosure that the La Bars had arrived in New York from Mexico City on Saturday afternoon, March 1. This meant that they had been in the city five days before La Bar finally tottered into Bellevue. During that time they had stayed at a hotel, which the Health Department has charitably never seen fit to identify. Fortunately, because of La Bar's unrelenting aches and pains, they seldom left their room. The only time they went outside the hotel, as far as Mrs. La Bar could recall, was on the Monday after their arrival here, when they took a stroll up Fifth Avenue and made a few trivial purchases at McCreery's, at a ten-cent store, and at the Knox hat shop. The report added that Mrs. La Bar's earlier reticence had been caused by a lifelong aversion to red tape.

A somewhat similar reticence was discovered in an assistant manager of the La Bars' hotel by a squad of Dr. Greenberg's agents who stopped by later that Wednesday. It was their intention to vaccinate all the hotel's employees and permanent residents and to gather the names and addresses of all transient guests registered there between March 1 and March 5. The opposition that they encountered was rigid, but it was not prolonged. It vanished at a thawing murmur from Dr. Greenberg over the telephone to the effect that the full text of Mrs. La Bar's memoir could easily be substituted for the tactfully expurgated version, omitting the name of the hotel, that was then being prepared for the press. His words induced a cordiality of such intensity that the manager himself trotted out the records and asked to be the first to bare his arm. By bedtime Wednesday night the inspectors had made a satisfying start on both their tasks, and they finished up the following day. Approximately three thousand people had spent one or more of the first five days of March under the same roof as La Bar. Nearly all were from out of town, and the names and addresses of these, who included residents of twenty-nine states, were transmitted to the health authorities of those states. Dr. Greenberg's men added what guests there had been from New York City to their already generous list of local suspects. In time all the three thousand, except for a few dozen adventurers who had registered under spurious names, were hunted down and, as it happily turned out, given a clean bill of health.

Meanwhile, Dr. Weinstein and Dr. Greenberg had decided that there wasn't much they could do in the way of disinfecting the La Bars' month-old trail up Fifth Avenue. They tried to console themselves with the realization that private physicians and the district health centers were experiencing another substantial increase in the demand for safety and certainty. This followed the newspaper publication, on Thursday, of Mrs. La Bar's censored revelations, which contained a discomfortingly vague reference to "a midtown hotel" in and about which La Bar had passed five days at nearly the peak of his contagiousness. Practically all the hotels in Manhattan at which a transient would be likely to stop are in the midtown area.

Bright and early Saturday morning, April 12, there was more unpleasant news. It was relayed to Dr. Weinstein by the New York State Department of Health, and it came from the village of Millbrook, in Dutchess County. A boy of four, Vernon L——, whose family lived in the Bronx, had been sick there for several days with what Dr. Smadel, in whom the state health authorities also had confidence, had just diagnosed as smallpox. The boy, an inmate of the Cardinal Hayes Convalescent Home, on the outskirts of town, was not, it appeared, critically ill. The source of the infection was no mystery. Before being admitted to the home, on March 13, Vernon had spent eighteen days, from February 21 to March 10, at Willard Parker, under treatment for scarlet fever. He was one of a number of Willard Parker alumni no longer in the city whom the state investigators had been asked to trace. The news of the Millbrook case was conveyed to Dr. Weinstein by telephone. The morning brought him two more agitating calls. One was from Dr. Muckenfuss and the other from Dr. Tolle. Dr. Muckenfuss reported that the municipal supply of vaccine was going fast. Two hundred thousand units had been distributed during the past week, and no more than that number were still on hand. Dr. Tolle called to say that Mrs. Acosta had just died.

At one-thirty that afternoon Dr. Weinstein, accompanied by Dr. Bernecker and a couple of his other associates, hopped around to Gracie Mansion for a candid chat with Mayor O'Dwyer, whom they found enduring an instant of repose. It had been Dr. Weinstein's original and commendable determination to spare the mayor any direct concern with the calamity. Dr. Muckenfuss's information, on top of everything else, had compelled him to change his mind. After Dr. Weinstein and his colleagues had successfully communicated their uneasiness to the mayor, they divulged a more specific reason for their visit. They asked for an appropriation of five hundred thousand dollars. Most of this sum, which, after a little ritualistic sparring, the mayor agreed to wheedle out of the Board of Estimate, would be expended for vaccine, Dr. Weinstein explained, and the rest for other extraordinary expenses of the Health and Hospital Departments, including the hiring of a thousand doctors and a couple hundred clerks to man additional public vaccination centers in various parts of the city. Then, also at the request of Dr. Weinstein, the mayor led the group down to City Hall, where at five o'clock he met in his office with the commissioners of all municipal departments and instructed them to see to it that no city employee delayed an instant in getting vaccinated. Before knocking off for the day the mayor called in the press, invited the photographers to unlimber their cameras, and allowed Dr. Weinstein to vaccinate him. This, he pointed out, was his fifth vaccination in six years, the others having been acquired during his service in the Army, but it was better to be safe than sorry.

Over the weekend the words and insinuating example of Mayor O'Dwyer, which were supplemented on the air at nine o'clock Sunday evening by a sudden, inflammatory chirp from Walter Winchell, resulted in a powerful quickening of the instinct for self-preservation, and this was still further heightened by word from the convalescent home in Millbrook that three more smallpox cases—two of them child inmates and the other an elderly nun on the staff of the institution—had been discovered there. Eighty-four thousand people, including hundreds in the remotest wastes of Staten Island, were vaccinated on Monday. On Tuesday, following the announcement of yet another case of smallpox originating at Bellevue—that of a sixty-year-old man who had been in the hospital suffering from a serious skin ailment for many months—two hundred thousand more were vaccinated. So great was the drain on the municipal reserves of vaccine that the mayor summoned before him representatives of all the big pharmaceutical firms that have plants or offices here and extracted from them a collective promise to make available to the city an abundant and immediate supply of the preparation. Pending the fulfillment of their pledge, he arranged, over the telephone, for an interim loan of vaccine from the Army and Navy. Wednesday night, in the course of announcing that emergency clinics would be opened the following morning in all of the city's eighty-four police stations, Dr. Weinstein found an opportunity tacitly to revise his earlier description of smallpox. It was, he now declared, "the most contagious of diseases." He was rewarded on Thursday evening with word that half a million vaccinations had been performed during the day.

There was no perceptible letup in the public's desire for immunization during the remainder of the week, and on Sunday, April 20, some additional interest was created by an announcement from Brigadier General Wallace H. Graham, the White House physician, that President Truman's preparations for a three-hour visit to New York the next day had included a brand-new vaccination. During the next week two hundred Health Department teams, each composed of a doctor and a nurse, moved through the public elementary and high schools, vaccinating some eight hundred and eighty-nine thousand children. Toward the end of the week Dr. Weinstein was sufficiently satisfied with the way things were going to reveal that the six surviving smallpox patients at Willard Parker and the four at Millbrook appeared to be out of danger. On Saturday, at his direction, the vaccinators were withdrawn from the police stations.

Six days later, on Friday, May 2, Dr. Weinstein formally announced the end of the outbreak and the completion of the biggest and fastest mass-vaccination campaign in the history of the world. Within the space of only twenty-eight days, he said, a total of at least six million three hundred and fifty thousand people had been vaccinated in the city. Practically everyone in New York was now immune. Although Dr. Weinstein had the delicacy not to say so, it was about time.

Twenty-four Hours
in a Cancer Hospital
by Evan McLeod Wylie

The hundred years following the middle of the nineteenth century saw the flowering of medicine as it now exists. In this period belong the discoveries of Pasteur, Koch, and Lister about which we have read. The feats of modern surgery and the discoveries of antibiotics by Fleming and his successors are all recent developments. New tools, techniques, and medicines have come into use in constantly increasing numbers. In hospitals and laboratories an army of scientists is uncovering facts about the cure of diseases which are reducing suffering and lengthening man's life expectancy. Sometimes these contributions are the work of individual research workers. More and more frequently they result from the concerted efforts of hundreds or thousands of men and women and the expenditure of millions of dollars. Such efforts culminated in the polio vaccines of Salk and Sabin. They are now being applied to finding the causes and cures for cancer. Memorial Hospital in New York City is one of the largest of the institutions which are devoted to treating the disease, combining the use of surgery, high-energy radiation, and chemotherapy to improve results. "Twenty-four Hours in a Cancer Hospital" gives us glimpses of the drama and the complexity of the problem.

9:10 A.M. "We're getting ready to go into his chest, Mike. All set?"

"Go ahead. I've got him."

Seated on a low stool beside his patient's head, the anesthetist rhythmically squeezes a black rubber bag, "breathing" for Donald Reade, Connecticut public-relations executive, aged fifty-two, who lies on his left side, sleeping quietly. A giant overhead light brilliantly illuminates a towel-draped, eighteen-inch incision that curves from a point just below Reade's shoulder blade all the way around to his breastbone. For more than one hour the only sounds in this cool, tiled room have been the click of clamps, the clink of discarded instruments, and the mask-muffled murmurs of the green-gowned surgeons and nurses gathered around the operating table. They have cut through skin, fat, and chest muscles, clamped and tied off dozens of blood vessels. Now, as the anesthetist takes over Reade's breathing, a scalpel nicks the last membrane. Scissors rapidly enlarge the opening. The right lung, gray, pink, dappled with a fine network of crisscrossing patterns, can be seen pulsing inside the chest cavity. . . .

This is operating room "B" on the twelfth floor of Memorial Center for Cancer and Allied Diseases. With its Sloan-Kettering Research Institute, hospitals, and clinics, and a graduate medical division, the Center occupies an entire city block near the East River in midtown Manhattan. It is one of the largest cancer centers in the world. Here at Memorial you can see how the cancer battle is going—how medical science is using the grants by individuals of great wealth, the sums contributed by government and industry and countless folk of lesser means to help cancer victims and find the cause of the cruelest disease of all that today has become, after heart disease, the most common cause of death in America.

This day at Memorial, no different from any other, began very early. At 6:30 A.M. the operating-room nurses began riding the elevators to the operating room, or "O.R.," floor to prepare for Donald Reade's lung surgery and thirty-five other highly complex cancer operations. Their schedules are always crowded, for surgery and X ray still offer the only certain cures for cancer. At 8:00 A.M. Reade, already relaxed and drowsy from a drug injection in the arm, was one of a steady stream of patients in beds and on rubber-tired stretchers being hustled into the operating rooms by fast-stepping male orderlies.

Donald Reade represents a new kind of patient at Memorial. It is suspected that he has lung cancer, now the most prevalent cancer in men, but he is not sick; he doesn't even have a symptom. Less than one week ago he and his wife sat in Memorial's Strang Prevention Clinic laughing and chatting with other men and women as they waited for the annual physical checkup which for them had become as routine as a visit to the dentist. Mrs. Reade's internal examination had included the painless Papanicalaou vaginal smear test by which cancer cells may be detected as much as eight to ten years before they become dangerous. Already it has saved the lives of tens of thousands of women. Mrs. Reade, as before, was ruled cancer free.

Her husband's complete examination stressed the lungs, rectum, prostate, and stomach—the four most common cancer sites in men. Strang's doctors found them all in top physical condition that morning, but two days later the X-ray lab reported a shadow in Reade's right lung.

"We aren't yet sure what it is," a Memorial surgeon told him, "but the safe thing is for you to come in and let us find out."

"I would have been wasting my time and yours coming here if I said no," Reade had replied. Three days later he entered the hospital.

9:30 A.M. "I feel nothing in the upper lobe . . ."

A big rib spreader, glittering in the bright light, makes it possible for the surgeon, a slight, intense man in his early forties, to thrust his gloved hand deep inside Donald Reade's chest and explore the right lung.

"Wait a moment . . . here it is . . . The middle lobe has a definite mass extending to the lower lobe. We'll get a reading from Pathology."

With a long, hollow suction needle on a glass slide, labeled neatly, packaged in a brown cartridge, it rockets fourteen floors through a pneumatic-tube system and lands with a thump and bang of an alarm bell in a bin in a first-floor laboratory. A waiting pathologist hurries the slide to a microscope.

With arms folded to preserve their gloves' germ-free surfaces, the surgeons in O.R. "B" stand waiting to hear his verdict. It comes by telephone in four minutes: "Cancer."

"All right," says the surgeon. "It's operable. Let's get started."

The team moves back to the table. The surgeons squirm their toes into their old operating shoes. Operating from breakfast until suppertime is hard on the arches.

"Take him down, Mike," the surgeon says.

There is a sudden gush of sweet-smelling anesthesia gases as the anesthetist deflates Reade's lungs to half size so that the team can go to work inside his chest.

10.00 A.M. "Come along now, Patsy. Bring our dolly."

A little girl with blond pigtails skips along the corridor in another wing of Memorial Center, clinging to the hand of a technician. Together they enter a thick-walled, lead-shielded cubicle. It is bare save for a very low bed. The technician arranges the child on her stomach, rolling up her blue sweater, packing a shield of ray-absorbing "bolus" bags around all but a small portion of the naked back. Electric motors whine. A huge X-ray tube descends slowly until it is within a few inches of the bed.

"Now just lie still, Patsy, until I come back in. Promise?"

"I promise. Give me my dolly."

The technician withdraws. A massive door grinds shut. On a black control board rows of red and green lights blink. There is a deep, muffled hum. Through a small, thick window the child can be seen stretched motionless, clasping the raggedy doll. For two minutes she remains exposed to a stream of million-volt rays.

This little girl has cancer. Already she is so badly afflicted that what appears to be a lighthearted hop and skip is actually a limp from damage the disease has done to her ankle. Now the disease has leaped to her hip. Does she have only a few months to live or will the radiation treatments destroy the malignant cells? The doctors cannot say. Many Memorial patients whose spreading cancers have made them bedridden paralytics have been so improved by radiation therapy that they have been able to return to normal living. At this moment, on the floor just above, a man of seventy-two is being treated for cancer with a massive dose of radiation from the Center's Cobalt Bomb. His disease, under control for years, dates back to 1933. Three of the Memorial doctors who originally treated him are now dead.

10:45 A.M. In a long, narrow, sunlit room high up in the Sloan-Kettering Institute white-coated girls move among wooden tables. Arranged on them neatly, like dinner place settings, are cages holding hundreds of squeaking, nibbling white mice. All have been implanted with "Sarcoma 180," a fast-growing animal cancer. Quickly the girls pluck out the mice. Thumb and forefinger of the left hand hold each by the scruff of the neck; the little finger crooks expertly around the tail.

A syringe held in the right hand pricks the animal's abdomen and shoots a new drug into it. Then the mouse is dropped back into the cage to resume its nibbling at a mound of food biscuits.

After seven days of these injections the mice will die painlessly in a chloroform chamber. Their tumors will be closely examined. If the new drug has reduced or cured the cancer, it will be set aside for further rigorous testing.

So far 15,000 such chemical compounds that Sloan-Kettering receives from laboratories and other research groups all over the world have been tested on its animals. Five or six new compounds each year are passed along for trial on volunteer human patients who could not be benefited by any other treatment. Eight so far have proved temporarily helpful to cancer patients, particularly children. (In the United States cancer is the leading cause of death from disease among children.)

11:15 A.M. The sun has dispersed the early-morning fog. On an outdoor terrace a dozen youngsters play happily with dolls, balls, and toy tractors.

"Your serve, Billy," a blue-smocked volunteer worker calls as she tosses the ball to two boys, aged seven and nine, playing ping-pong in wheel chairs.

Both these boys have acute leukemia, cancer of the blood. Like the quiet little girl watching them from a crib, they, too, were pale, emaciated, and much weakened from the merciless bleeding under the eyes, inside the mouth, on the hands, and from the nose that accompanies this disease. Now they are regaining their normal health. They should be able to resume a perfectly normal life with their families and schoolmates—for one or even two years. After that the new drugs suddenly cease to work. The disease will return, perhaps in a more virulent form. As in the case of the five-year-old boy in an oxygen tent in a nearby room, it runs a swift and inexorable course to death.

Why fight to keep these pathetic children alive if they are doomed to die so soon? Perhaps before the drugs fail, the doctors answer, we will have something really good to offer them, a longer life or even a complete cure.

11:30 A.M. "I went out for a moment for some coffee. Has there been a call for me from upstairs?" Mrs. Donald Reade, a tall, handsome woman in a dark print summer dress, stands anxiously at the desk in Memorial's main lobby.

"Not yet, Mrs. Reade," replies the receptionist. "But there's nothing to worry about. They often take a long time, you know."

"That's what the doctor warned me last night, but I came in from Connecticut early anyway. It wouldn't have been any easier waiting at home."

"Do you have anyone in the city you might visit for a few hours? It may be some time still," the receptionist suggests.

Mrs. Reade glances around at the busy lobby. "Well, we know people in New York, but I think I'll sit this one out by myself. My married daughter is in Los Angeles. Don didn't want me to, but I telephoned her last night after I left the hospital . . ."

She stands at the desk talking for a while before returning to her magazine on one of the yellow sofas.

11:45 A.M. "How much blood has he had, Mike?"

"Two pints. I'm starting another one right now." The anesthetist reaches up to the tall stands from which bottles of dark red blood from the hospital blood bank are dripping slowly into Donald Reade's veins.

The surgeons have run into a problem. The lobes of Reade's right lung are fused together. Separating their webs of blood vessels and branches of air bronchi is painfully slow work. The little suture nurse is calmly keeping track of more than two hundred instruments. Circulating nurses move silently around the room, replenishing the neat piles of compresses on the instrument stand,

refilling the basins with warm, sterile water, keeping the anesthetist supplied with bottles of blood and other intravenous
solutions. Donald Reade sleeps on as peacefully as if he were in
his own bed.

Three masked strangers take seats in a narrow gallery. They
are surgeons from Haiti and Panama who have come to Memorial, as do so many other doctors from different countries, to
study the latest techniques in cancer treatments.

Minutes slip by as a string of dark lymph glands are removed
to catch any cancer cells that may have strayed from the main
tumor. As city air-raid sirens signal the noon hour, a fresh suture
nurse quietly steps up to the stand. The surgeon is suddenly
aware that a different hand is slapping scissors and clamps into
his palm. "Good lord, is it that late already? We're drifting on
and on here, but we can't go any faster."

1:00 P.M. The grueling hours of surgery, the thousands of
new chemicals are only part of the many-pronged attack at
Memorial. "No Visitors," warns a large sign on Sloan-Kettering's
thirteenth floor, where researchers, protected by special inoculations, are growing viruses, the microscopic organisms that cause
ailments ranging from poliomyelitis to deadly tropical diseases.

A girl holds up a small bottle half full of cloudy amber fluid.
"See the gunk in the bottom of the bottle?" she asks us. "Those
are dead human cancer cells we have destroyed with one of our
viruses, Egypt 101; it causes inflammation of the brain. Viruses
have to eat, too. We feed ours exclusively on human cancer
growing in these test tubes until some of the viruses develop a
real appetite for it. We hope to get one that will seek out all the
tumor cells in a human patient and destroy them without harming the rest of the body."

What about the natural molds that produced penicillin and the
other wonder drugs? Could any of these also hold a cure for

cancer? Sloan-Kettering is trying to find out. In a cool chamber hundreds of green and white molds are growing in flasks and bottles. Along with the viruses they are turned over to the laboratories which work with dozens and dozens of chicken eggs, cages full of mice and rats, and incubators of test tubes. A technician working with the eggs cuts a tiny window in the shell of each egg. With tweezers she plants a bit of cancer tissue on the membrane of a growing chick embryo and then returns the egg to a warm incubator. As the cancer grows larger along with the chick, the viruses and molds can be tested by injecting them into the egg yolk.

1:30 P.M. "It does help to talk to someone else, doesn't it?" a conversation begins.

Donald Reade's wife shows the strain she is under by rolling and unrolling the magazine on her lap as she tries to chat with a woman from Wyoming whose husband is also undergoing surgery.

"Poor Don, he was joking last night that he'd never been in a hospital before. He's certainly getting a rough baptism."

1:45 P.M. "Careful—don't nip that vein." In O.R. "B" the surgeon's voice, still deliberately casual, betrays the strain of five solid hours of surgery. The huge incision in Donald Reade's chest, neatly draped with fresh green towels, is filled with clusters of long clamps. A skein of black suture threads, fastened to something invisible inside the cavity, is firmly entwined in the young resident's left hand. More instruments are being sterilized in an autoclave in an anteroom. It suddenly hisses loudly and emits a cloud of steam.

"It's getting like a dry-cleaning establishment in here," snaps the surgeon. "What's happening to our air conditioning?"

The room is actually very cool, but under the intensely bright lights in a long-sleeved, neck-to-knees gown it's quite another story. An acute silence falls over the table as the three men, working so close together that elbows and forearms intertwine, reach a critical point in the surgery. Time seems to stand still. A flock of city pigeons swoops and circles outside the long windows. On nearby roof tops city dwellers appear with books and sun-bathing chairs. Suddenly bright red blood bubbles and froths in the chest cavity.

"Clamps, please!" There is a note of urgency in the barked request. Instruments and sponges fly through the fingers of the suture nurse.

"Suction, please! I can't see what I'm doing."

The unchecked hemorrhage is filling the chest. The anesthetist anxiously eyes his gauges. The young resident thrusts a long, curved silver suction tube deep into the cavity. It gurgles and squeaks in the deepening pool of blood.

"I've got it." Clamps seize the severed artery. Suture threads tie it off. The silver tube noisily sucks only air. The incision is sponged into a dry, bloodless state. There is a last snip of scissors and then the middle and lower lobes of Reade's right lung are lifted free by the skeins of black threads and laid on a wax-covered tray held by a circulating nurse. She carries it to the ante-room, washes it, and returns it to a nearby table.

With the lobes out, the tension in the room is dissipated. The surgeon steps over and with a long knife slices deep into the lobe, exposing human cancer—a gritty, gray mass about the size of a golf ball. "There it is—there's the nasty customer." He bursts enthusiastically into French for the benefit of the visiting surgeons: "*Voilà . . . vous voyez . . . pardonnez* my emergency-room French. It looks very good. I think we have got all of it out."

In better spirits he returns to the operating table. "Well, we can prepare for an exit now. We'd have been out of here long ago if Dr. Fowler hadn't kept stepping on the suction tube."

The resident's eyes crinkle in a mask-concealed grin. "Fifteen years of training and I'm a bust."

"Not at all. You're probably a whiz with boils."

They settle down to the hour that will be required to close the incision. Then Donald Reade will go to a soundproofed recovery pavilion where anesthetist and specially trained nurses will guide his recovery to consciousness.

2:30 P.M. Two weeks ago a young woman was dying of breast cancer that had spread to her bones, skin, and spinal column. Then she underwent a radically new operation; her pituitary gland, a pea-sized growth gland buried deep within her skull, was removed, thereby cutting off a supply of hormones that apparently were feeding her tumors. Already their growth has been halted. Now, smiling gratefully up at the doctors, she tells a Sloan-Kettering team gathered at her bedside, "Suddenly the world seems clear again . . . like a fog has lifted. I ate all my supper last night . . . That bad pain in my back has gone away . . . I feel so much better."

The glow in the woman's face, the faint color returning to her cheeks, the curious arrested look of the cancerous lesions on her body must repay the doctors for long hours of research and former fruitless experiments. But the question in each of their minds is, "Why did this happen?"

Whether her cancer has been halted for one day, one week, a month, or indefinitely, they do not know. Some of the incurably ill men and women who have had this operation are alive and well almost two years later with their disease still quiet. Others quickly relapsed and died. Another woman, treated with hormone injections three years ago, is back at her job completely without symptoms. Only with much more research and many costly experiments can the doctors find out why these things happen.

Farther down the same corridor another white-coated team pushes a cart on which rides a heavy, thick-walled lead pot from a United States Atomic Energy furnace. They roll it into the room of a slim, brown-haired schoolteacher from Pennsylvania.

"Ready for your big drink, Mrs. Briggs?" a tall young doctor asks.

The teacher, her face quite thin and drawn, pushes herself up on her pillows, smoothing her pink bed jacket, blushing at the sudden influx of male visitors. She eyes the lead pot uncertainly. "I guess so."

A doctor pulls on rubber gloves. His assistant holds a Geiger counter that measures radioactivity. With long tongs they reach swiftly inside the pot, lift out a beaker of liquid and pour it into a glass. It is crystal-clear. It doesn't bubble. It sits there as bland as a glass of cold water. The Geiger counter emits a sharp clickety-click warning at its presence. The teacher resolutely seizes the glass, lifts it to her lips, and swallows steadily until it is empty. Instantly the doctor returns the glass to the lead pot and claps on the cover. The Geiger counter subsides.

"How was it, Mrs. Briggs?"

"A funny taste. Will it make me very sick?"

"Probably only a sore throat in a few days. We'll fix you up. Don't worry."

Afterward he explains to us, "That lady has thyroid cancer. The radioactive solution, I-131, she just drank will destroy her thyroid gland and its cancer cells. The next dose we give her should follow any thyroid cancer cells that may have strayed to other parts of her body. If her cancer doesn't move too fast, we may be able to help her."

4:30 P.M. "Mrs. Reade—" The surgeon, changed to a summer street suit, smiles reassuringly. "It's all over and your husband is doing fine. I'm sorry we took so long, but lung operations always do. I've got very good news for you. We found a small tumor that could have been dangerous. We think we were able to remove it completely."

"Then it was cancer, Doctor?"

"Yes, but when it's caught in such an early stage it's often completely curable. It didn't show any signs of having spread, and I think the lab report will confirm that later on."

He shakes a finger at her reprovingly. "Now, the receptionist tells me you sat here all day. I want you to get out of here, go to a movie, have dinner, and then come back. By that time your husband will be wide-awake and ready to leave the recovery room and you can see him."

He walks with her to a telephone booth. She presses his hand and steps inside. "Hello—long distance? I want to place a call to Los Angeles . . ."

5:10 P.M. The sun is sliding down behind the city towers. The ceaseless mutter of the avenues' traffic mounts to the rush-hour roar. Memorial's workers, heading for home, exchange greetings in the elevators.

"Hello, Charlie. Did you find the miracle cure today?"

"Sure did. But one of the girls washed it down the sink by mistake. See you tomorrow. . . ."

On the second floor an emergency is unfolding for a ten-man team from Sloan-Kettering's physiology laboratory. Surgical-physiology teams are composed of young surgeons, residents, internes, medical students, and technicians. Their aim is to find new ways of meeting the fatal crises that occur in the body chemistry and vital organs of cancer patients. In a conference room holding a wall of bookshelves, a neglected aquarium, a long table littered with medical journals, notebooks, stethoscopes, cups of stale coffee, and a vase of lilacs, they met today to cope with a crisis in a liver-cancer patient.

She is a fifty-seven-year-old housewife from Oklahoma. Because the liver is a huge sponge with a terribly complicated circulatory system and at least seventy vital functions, most surgeons leave it alone. Liver cancer has always been considered hopeless. Memorial now is dispelling such beliefs. One week ago its surgeons removed 80 per cent of this woman's liver and prepared to meet any postoperative difficulties with such emergency measures as this team will now undertake.

Yesterday she lapsed into a coma. Now the report from her bedside reads, ". . . Losing ground rapidly. There is a swelling of the lower limbs. Her breathing is becoming deep and rapid."

The team's diagnosis: renal shutdown. The shock of the big operation has been too much for her kidneys. They have ceased to function. Swiftly accumulating body poisons soon will bring death.

Their decision: try the artificial kidney.

Now the "kidney," a white cabinet about the size of a small washing machine surmounted by a thick rubber-and-cellophane sandwich squeezed tightly together with massive orange clamps, is rolled down the corridor. Behind it trail three technicians pushing a huge tub of filtering fluid.

There is not much time left. Unaware of the doctors and nurses crowding into her small bedroom, the Oklahoma woman is sinking rapidly. Her fingers work weakly at the white coverlet. Her lips move in a faint whisper. ". . . I don't like birds. Keep that bird off my feet, please."

Quickly nurses assist two surgeons in preparing vein and artery connections in her left arm. The "kidney" and the huge tub are rolled close to the bed. Physicians give injections. Technicians kneel on the floor linking up the intricate coils of tubing.

"Arteries all open, George?"

"Check."

"Veins all open?"

"Check."

"Okay, we're going on the machine. Take the speed up to ten." The "kidney's" electric motors whir. Blood suddenly transforms the plastic tubes entwined around the white cabinet into bright red garlands. Metallic fingers drum rhythmically, ingeniously simulating the pulse of an artery. As the woman's poison-laden blood is detoured through the thousands of tiny passages in the rubber-cellophane sandwich, a miracle of chemistry causes the waste products to be exchanged with elements in the fluid from the big tub. At least six hours of steady operation, with the blood from her body flowing through the "kidney" at the rate of a pint a minute will be required to save this gravely ill woman's life. Meanwhile the doctors must inject clot-preventing drugs every twenty minutes, rush blood samples back to their laboratory to measure the "kidney's" effectiveness, and keep a hawk-like watch on her heart and lungs.

6:50 P.M. While they work, the corridors outside the room echo with footsteps and the murmur of many voices. For some of the sick people, now reunited with their families and friends, the evening visiting hour is a poignant, much-awaited moment. But many of Memorial's patients have been sent there by their doctors from faraway towns and cities and from South America, Europe, and Asia. Their loneliness is eased by Memorial's corps of volunteers, 300 New Yorkers ranging from businessmen to waitresses who endeavor to fill the sick people's time with art, recreation, and handicraft programs, and run coffee counters, movie projectors, gift shops, libraries, and perform hundreds of small services for them.

This evening one volunteer, a retired broker, sits reading the newspapers aloud to a man undergoing a blood transfusion. Earlier he arranged for plane reservations for a woman flying home to Indiana and picked up another's wrist watch at an outside repair shop. Later on tonight he will make long-distance telephone calls to report the conditions of several patients to anxious families unable to journey to New York.

This man, who by now has spent more time with cancer's victims than most doctors, says, "The most extraordinary thing about them is their courage. Even if you attribute it partly to religious faith or to a lack of awareness of their plight, there's still a peculiar strength that Nature seems to lend these people. You seldom see them give way to despair. You rarely hear one use the word 'cancer' when talking about his 'sickness.' It's as if the human mind refuses to acknowledge such a terrifying enemy so that it can better concentrate on a fight for life."

9:P.M. "Now don't you go away." A soft-voiced, colored orderly smiles down at Donald Reade, whom he has just strapped into a cocoon of blankets on a stretcher. Fully conscious, in no great pain thanks to the week-lasting anesthetic that the surgeons injected into nerves inside the chest, Donald Reade is leaving the recovery pavilion. His wife is waiting for him in his own room with the surgeon's prediction that in a few weeks he will be back at his desk. Even the loss of the fifth rib is temporary. Nature will fabricate a substitute shortly.

11:30 P.M. It is close to midnight, but the Center, like the great city surrounding it, cannot succumb to sleep. Nurses shuttle back and forth with trays of liquids and hypodermics, rendering the care needed in cancer hospitals where rubber tubes and glass bottles replace the body's ravaged organs.

A young resident physician moves at a rapid clip through the deserted corridors, past the silent laboratories, dodging the mops and whirling floor waxers of the cleaning force. He smiles at an elderly patient, her face utterly tranquil, who works steadily at a heap of embroidered aprons. Then he pauses beside a young man with a bent figure and sharply bony face who sits alone in a wheel chair staring out the window at the brightly lit terraces and roof gardens of a lush apartment house. "How's the leg tonight, Frank?"

"Not too good, Doc. That swelling seems higher up again."

The doctor stoops to probe his leg and groin. "Got your score card?"

Bony shoulders move beneath a faded bathrobe as the youth draws forth the small packet of papers on which he records the daily liquid intake and output of his body. While the doctor checks the neatly penciled figures, the patient continues to study the flashing neon signs and magical glow of midtown Manhattan where others are enjoying themselves, planning for the future.

"You think you can stop that swelling Doc?" The query is detached, impersonal, without anxiety.

"Sure thing, Frank. We'll see you tomorrow," the doctor replies.

He says to us later, "That kid's fought Hodgkin's for five years. Now it's closing in on him."

He pokes his head into the room where the physiology team, working furiously, have just removed a blood clot from their "kidney." Now its muffled whirring has resumed again.

"My eyeballs are draggin'. Anybody here for coffee?"

"Not now, old sport. We just got hooked in here again." The team, draped over chairs, squatting on their heels and sitting on the floor of the crowded sickroom, are bleary-eyed but elated. Lab tests confirm that the "kidney" is draining the poisonous wastes out of their patient's blood. If they can keep it working through the night, she will begin to emerge from the coma. In a few days her own kidneys should begin to function once again.

Along with Donald Reade's, her name can be chalked up in the winning column in the ceaseless battle against cancer. On this average day at Memorial, twenty-eight more men, women, and children have descended the Center's wide front steps completely cured of cancer or for a time, at least, restored to health and normal living. Three hard fights have been lost. One little boy in the Children's Pavilion died this afternoon.

12:15 A.M. A flashlight bobs down a dim corridor. The supervising nurse, a crisp young brunette, has been summoned to the fourth floor. She slips quickly into a brilliantly illuminated room. Oxygen bubbles through a glass bottle. Two nurses support a powerfully built man in his late forties as he struggles desperately for breath. Gaily decorated get-well cards and a silver-framed photograph of two children have been hastily thrust aside to make room for basins and trays of medicines.

"It started just a few minutes ago," the floor nurse whispers to the supervisor. "We can't seem to do anything for him."

Bending low over the bed, the supervisor makes a quick examination. A moment later she is at the floor desk telephone. "We're getting a temperature of 105, Doctor . . . His lungs seem to be filling up . . . I think he's going . . ."

She flashes back to the big man's bed. "The doctor's coming right up, Mr. Baxter. He'll help you."

He tries to nod his thanks. His face wears the defenseless, intensely preoccupied look of the very ill. The nurse steps to an anteroom where a woman sits weeping silently and looking out the window. A great bridge, still streaming with traffic, forms an arch of moving lights over the black silhouettes of tugs and barges riding the crest of a flood tide.

"Mrs. Baxter?" the nurse asks gently.

The man's wife turns a white face, twisted with grief. "I had to come out for a minute."

She rises and follows the nurse back to the bedside. Elevator doors clash in the corridor's night silence as a young resident hurries after them. After a while the supervisor returns. She says to us in a flat voice, "I guess you saw the picture of the kids by his bed."

She stands looking at the river and the bridge. "When I first came to New York," she says, "I used to pass Memorial and I'd say to myself, 'There's one place I never want to get involved with.'

"Then one day I thought, If you're a nurse, why pretend the disease doesn't exist? I tried temporary duty here and I've never left. Sometimes you don't think you can face another night of it, but I've found something here I haven't felt since the war—a sense of being part of a big fight.

"Everybody here is working together against one thing. You feel it when you walk in the front door and I think the sick people feel it, too. It's what keeps a lot of them going and a lot of us going, too.

"Once you come up against cancer you either want to run like the devil or you want to be around every time it's licked, especially when they smash it for good."

Altogether, with funds supplied by government, industry, rich individuals and famous public subscriptions such as the American Cancer Society and the Damon Runyon Memorial Fund, this country is still spending only about $25 million a year to defeat cancer.

In contrast, Americans this year will spend $23½ million for playing cards. The Department of Agriculture will spend $65 million for farm research. The entire cost of the Sloan-Kettering research program for one year adds up to less than the cost of one Air Force bomber or a fraction of what New Yorkers have spent in this one day on entertainment.

Memorial Center, one of our greatest hopes for a cure for cancer, exists largely on annual, private contributions, but it now does not have enough in reserve for more than one year of operation.

All of the efforts of its dedicated workers, magnificent as they are, seem like shamefully puny gestures for the richest nation on earth to make against the most implacable and terrifying natural enemy now facing mankind.

The Death
of Louis Slotin

by Ralph E. Lapp

Advances in any science are not always an unmixed blessing, and medical science is no exception. A perfect example of this truism is the advent, within the past two decades, of atomic medicine. The beneficial uses of radioactivity have been manifold. Radioactive chemicals, as we have seen, are proving helpful in the treatment of cancer. Radioactive isotopes are being used to unravel the most obscure chemical reactions of the body. But as we are constantly being informed, radioactivity can also be a deadly peril which, in sufficient quantities, could conceivably wipe out the human race. The women who were employed in a New Jersey factory making radium watch dials and the inhabitants of Hiroshima have been examples which point this moral. Louis Slotin, whose case is described in the following selection, is still another. The experiences of these individuals typify one of the greatest problems of modern man.

Ordinary or natural uranium is quite harmless for it will not, by itself, sustain chain reaction. Only when it is embodied in an enormous matrix of some light element such as graphite or heavy water does it sustain a slow chain reaction. Were this to be allowed to run out of control, it would not in general produce anything like an explosion. Heat would be produced and some inner parts of the reactor might melt, but it would not qualify as a bomb.

Enriched uranium or plutonium is quite different from ordinary uranium. Assemble too much of it in one place, and the chain reaction will automatically run away. Thus, it was rather important for the people at Oak Ridge and at Hanford to know how much was "enough" so that safety precautions could be taken. At Los Alamos the experts refined their calculations as to the size of the critical mass, but it was essential to have experimental measurements.

The man who headed up the "critical assembly" group was a good friend of mine. I knew Louis Slotin while an undergraduate at the University of Chicago and liked him very much for his pleasant manner and friendly advice. He was never too busy to help out a Ph.D. aspirant, and I remember that he gave me valuable pointers on making Geiger counters. On my visits to Los Alamos I used to stop by to see Slotin and give him the news of Chicago. He was a short, wiry youth with dark hair and soft, sad eyes. Somehow or other he always ended up doing jobs nobody else wanted. He never complained, and I respected the cheerful way that Slotin did dirty work.

Slotin had nerves of iron and he needed them for his critical experiments with the "nukes." Here is essentially what he did in making a critical assembly, or in "tickling the dragon's tail," as we called it. He would set up a table with a neutron counter and a rack. On the rack he would place two pieces of bomb stuff, each one being somewhat less than a critical amount. Then he would push the two pieces, often in the form of hemispheres the size of a split baseball, toward each other. As the gap narrowed between the pieces, he would measure the buildup of the chain reaction inside the assembly. He used a small source of neutrons to amplify the effect, rather than waiting for stray neutrons to come from cosmic rays or from the material itself. He determined the tempo of the buildup by listening to the clicks in an amplifier connected to the neutron counter and in watching a recorder trace out a jagged red line on a moving roll of graph paper.

As the hemispheres came closer and closer, more and more of the neutrons would tend to be caught within the bomb stuff and fewer would be lost through the narrowing air gap. The chain reaction would build up, and, just before it was ready to rip, Slotin would calmly stop the experiment, measure the separation, and deduce just how big the critical mass was. He grew quite adept at the experiment for he repeated it fifty times or more. His nonchalance amazed Enrico Fermi, who once warned him, "Keep doing that experiment that way and you'll be dead within a year." Some of Slotin's colleagues tried to get him to build in automatic safety devices, like powerful springs, which could be triggered to hurl the two hemispheres apart when the neutrons built up too fast. He turned aside this suggestion with this retort: "If I have to depend upon safety devices I am sure to have an accident."

Slotin was asked to repeat the experiment "just one more time" to demonstrate the technique to others in the laboratory. So he gathered the group of six people behind him in the sunlit room where he did his work. One man, Dr. Alvin Graves, had his hand almost on his shoulder as Slotin proceeded to demonstrate his technique. He used two hemispheres that he had worked with before and holding a screw driver he moved the two pieces of bomb material together to form a "nuke" or nuclear core. Slowly, at first, then more quickly, the counters clicked away and the red line moved upward on the white paper chart.

Suddenly the counters screamed and the red-ink indicators swung off scale. There had been an accident! The chain reaction was running away. Almost as if by reflex action Slotin hurled himself forward and tore the reacting mass apart with his bare hands. The others gasped and, turning around, Slotin, his face whitely reflecting his terror, motioned them to leave the room.

Slotin telephoned the hospital and said that there had been an accident. Then he telephoned his close friend, Phil Morrison. He was nauseated but, always the true scientist, paused in the hallway and drew a pencil sketch of the room and marked everyone's position, putting a big X for himself. Then he scribbled the time, 3:20 P.M., and hustled the group off to the hospital, all of them jamming into two jeeps.

The big question in the mind of everyone was: how much dose did Slotin get? The neutrons and X rays which flashed through his body before he tore the assembly apart caused biological damage to his body. This we measure in certain units—called roentgens or r-units. A total of about 400 r over the entire body is considered the lethal amount for most people. This deadly amount does not produce immediate effect but takes time . . . weeks . . . or days . . . depending on the dose.

Phil Morrison, gifted theoretical physicist, worked feverishly to reconstruct the accident and to learn how serious was his friend's plight. Slotin's very blood had been made radioactive by the burst of neutrons which riddled his body, and a small sample of his blood gave a clue to the dose. Of course Slotin was hospitalized and became ill rather soon, but during the first few days he was cheerful and would ask when visited by Morrison, "Well, what's the dose?" Nobody really knew, and it took a long time to find out. Before they did, the tide had changed in Slotin's reaction to the radiation. His differential blood-cell count told the story—a picture so hopeless that the attending Army nurse, hardened to hospital routine, broke down and sobbed when she saw the results.

Slotin had been most severely irradiated around the hands and arms. These parts of his pain-ridden body swelled grotesquely and the skin sloughed off. The nation's best doctors were flown to the Army hospital at Los Alamos but they could do little for the weakening patient. Nor could we do much more today.

Technicians strung a telephone connection into the bare hospital room and Slotin talked with his mother in Winnipeg, Canada. The next day his parents were flown to New Mexico by special Army plane, and they stayed at their son's bedside until he breathed his last. The end came early on the morning of the ninth day after the accident.

The man who stood behind Slotin, Dr. Graves, was severely injured by the accident but he recovered and went on to become associate director of Los Alamos in the postwar period. He had this to say of Slotin: "I can perhaps tell you as much about his personality and character as I could in very many words if I merely quote to you his first statement when we were alone together in the hospital room. He said, 'I'm sorry I got you into this. I am afraid that I have less than a fifty-fifty chance of living. I hope you do better than that.' "

Slotin was not destined to be a great or a famous man. He was one of the many scientists who worked devotedly and unselfishly throughout the war. The young scientist gave his life, just as did many of his comrades in arms.

Slotin's experiment was outlawed at Los Alamos. With the development of television and remote-control gadgetry, it became possible to do the critical assembly operations with no one within a quarter of a mile. White-coated technicians, principally women, control the assembly and make all their observations without the slightest danger to themselves.

The Cruel Game

by Heinz Gartmann

Like atomic medicine, space medicine is a branch of the science which was totally unknown until a few years ago. However, the basic problems involved in keeping man alive in space are already becoming clear. Can human beings survive the huge acceleration of rocket projectiles? How will they feel in a state of weightlessness? What are the dangers of meteorites piercing and destroying space ships? What will the new-day explorers eat and drink? How will they survive the sheer boredom of long voyages in restricted quarters? How can they be protected against the radiation of outer space? These are some of the questions for which answers are being sought. Experiments on living creatures, and especially on human beings, are still in a rudimentary state, but the monkeys Able and Baker and the dog Laika have proved that they can survive under conditions of space travel. Brave men and women are also offering themselves for testing. "The Cruel Game" tells about a few of these heroes of experimental medicine.

Annually, in Washington, D.C., the Cheney Medal is awarded for extraordinary courage, for bravery and selfless devotion to the service of humanity. On August 26, 1955, this honor was conferred on a scientist, Dr. John Paul Stapp. This quiet, modest, forty-five-year-old lieutenant colonel in the American Air Force is chief of the Aero Medical Field Laboratory at Holloman Air Development Center in New Mexico. The Cheney Medal marked the fourth time he had been decorated for his pioneering work.

There can be no doubt that John Paul Stapp is one of the bravest men in the world, a man so dedicated to his work that no personal sacrifice is too great. But outwardly there is nothing conspicuously heroic about him. He is of medium height, friendly, reticent; anyone seeing him for the first time would take him for a lecturer who is spending a few semesters at the field laboratory in order to work out practical solutions to a few scientific problems. Stapp is, as a matter of fact, also that; he studied chemistry and zoology and taught for six years at the University of Texas. Just incidentally he acquired a doctorate in biophysics. Later he was able to realize an old wish and in 1944 received his M.D. But he never had the chance to set up in practice; since it was wartime, Stapp took a training course in air medicine and became an Air Force doctor. In 1953 he assumed charge of a vital research project: to determine the direct consequences of extremely high speeds and accelerations upon the human body. He brought the experimental subject right along with him to the laboratory: John Paul Stapp.

At the entrance to the Holloman Air Force Base a stubby-winged dummy rocket stands as memorial to the fact that here, in September, 1947, the first rocket plane was flown. The whole area, in fact, is a remarkable corner of the United States. About an hour's drive to the south stretch the 4,000 square miles of White Sands, the proving grounds for big rockets. And in the northwest corner of the 1,200-square-mile Alamogordo airfield is located the historic "Point Zero" of the atomic age; there it was, on July 16, 1945, that the mushroom cloud of the first nuclear explosion billowed about ten miles high into the stratosphere.

In the Aero Medical Field Laboratory of the Holloman Air Development Center, which in 1955 was merged with the White Sands Proving Grounds to form a vast test area for Army, Navy, and Air Force, John Paul Stapp has been putting himself through the most frightful stress tests any man ever conceived. Stubbornly, he is seeking the answer to the question: What kind of shocks can a man endure, what are the effects of mechanical forces upon living tissue, and how can man be protected against abrupt deceleration and wind blast so that he will survive the terrible stress this age of technology can impose upon him?

When in bygone days a stagecoach collided with an obstacle, serious accidents could result, so that rattled travelers often referred bitterly to the coaches as "bonebreakers." Nevertheless, the shocks that the bodies of travelers had to endure in those days were relatively minor. Today, on the other hand, if a man has to save his life by parachuting from a plane flying at sonic speeds, the sudden violence of the wind blast is enough to break his neck.

At this point technological man has reached a critical boundary which he must cross. It is not high speed that is the menace, but too powerful acceleration or its reverse, deceleration, the merciless shock of a sudden jolt.

To see what such jolts could do to the human body, Colonel Stapp became in 1954 the fastest man on the surface of the earth. When a man is hurled out of a fast-moving plane at a great height, it is impossible to measure exactly the forces he is subject to and their immediate effects upon him. Stapp therefore needed a powerful decelerator, a machine that could attain extremely high speeds on the ground and be braked within an unprecedentedly short span of time. He found this machine in the form of a sled mounted on rails and powered by rocket drive.

The Holloman Air Development Center possessed a 3,500-foot stretch of tracks and a rocket-powered sled which was intended originally for study of air currents and resistance in airplane and projectile parts. This apparatus was placed at Colonel Stapp's disposal. By the end of 1953 he had utilized it for more than two hundred successful experiments upon living subjects: chimpanzees, volunteers, and of course himself. No one could say the colonel asked more of others or of defenseless animals than he did of himself. By early 1954 the experimental program had progressed to the point where harsher tests could be expected to clarify the last remaining questions.

The new decelerator was built by Northrop Aircraft, Inc. It consisted of a 2,000-pound test sled containing a seat for the subject and measuring instruments, and the actual rocket sled itself, which pushed the test sled. The rocket sled could take twelve powder rockets which together delivered a thrust of 54,000 pounds, precisely the thrust of the thirteen-ton V-2. Both parts of the test vehicle were held to the rails by grips, so that they could not jump the track during the ride. At the end of the run the tracks continued on over a concrete ditch which could be filled with water to any desired depth. Braking scoops on the two sleds smashed unhindered through the masonite dams which precisely regulated the height of the water and brought the onrushing vehicles to a quicker or slower stop, depending upon the water level.

That would be the point of merciless stress, the painful, seemingly endless second when the human organism in the torture seat of the rocket sled was so racked by pain that he teetered on the verge of unconsciousness and looked death in the eye.

More than four months had been devoted to preliminary tests with unmanned sleds. On March 18, 1954, all necessary preparations had been completed for the first test with a human subject. Colonel Stapp was ready to take his chance.

The procedure began with a careful check of Stapp's heartbeat, circulation, reflexes, and respiration. Six hours before the start he received his last meal; four hours before, his last drop of water. A full sixty minutes beforehand he climbed onto the sled.

Facing the direction in which he would ride, he was belted in with double-strength nylon webbing. Assistants tied his elbows behind his back, bound his wrists fast to his thighs, strapped his legs together at the ankles and above and below the knees, and secured his feet to the running boards. Then they attached the various instruments: accelerometers on his chest, behind the seat, and on the framework of the sled itself; tensiometers attached to the safety belts; a Pitot tube for measuring wind pressure in front of the carefully "bundled" body.

Stapp's head was unprotected. It was not strapped, and he wore no helmet. His entire body was shielded by an eighty-pound windbreak made of solid sheet metal.

While these preparations were being made, the technicians at the back of the sled carefully attached the fuse wires to the six powder rockets which together would deliver a thrust of 27,000 pounds, twice the force of the motor of a jet plane.

A few minutes before the start the men withdrew to the underground blockhouse 200 feet west of the southern end of the length of track. Stapp remained alone on his monstrous vehicle. While he concentrated upon the ordeal before him, the clockwork mechanism of the experiment began running its course in the blockhouse. Loudly, tersely, like quick hammer blows, a technician counted down the last few seconds before firing: Ten, nine, eight, seven—and with each successive hammer blow another apparatus was switched on, in accordance with a carefully prepared schedule: cameras, speed indicator, electronic accelerometers, telautographs. Through the loud-speaker Stapp could hear time running out. Later, after the experiment, he was to report: "During the last ten seconds of the countdown, the subject tensed, bit hard on the bite block, braced his head against the padded headrest, and concentrated on pulling the cord to start the motion-picture camera on the front of the sled at the count of five." Stapp always speaks of the "subject," never of himself, and there is no mention of fear, although such a feeling would be all too natural.

At "zero" Stapp heard the six rockets ignite with a curious whining tone which quickly developed into the customary dull roar. Then he felt the increasing pressure at his back, and recognized by the light shock that the sled was moving.

The thundering rockets blasted for only five seconds. Acceleration mounted to 5 g. By "g" is meant the acceleration which the earth's gravity imposes upon a freely falling body; in the vicinity of the earth's surface it amounts to 32.2 feet per second; that is to say, the speed of a freely falling body increases by 32.2 feet per second.

By the time the six jets of flame went out, the sled had traveled a distance of 1,800 feet and attained a speed of 615 feet per second. All this while Stapp was holding his breath and staring at the bolt heads and inner structure of the windshield in front of his face. Without turning his head, he had a blurred vision of the landscape swirling by on his right and left.

When the propulsive force stopped, his situation changed instantly. The head and shoulders of "the subject" were pitched violently forward. His body hung heavily in the harness, because now the resistance of the air and the friction of the rails on the sled grips were vigorously braking the coasting sled. This phase of the experiment lasted 1½ seconds. Then the braking scoops of the drive sled encountered the first basin of water. "A distinct bump was felt when the propulsion sled separated from the test sled." Stapp later reported: "Pressure of the straps against shoulders and hips increased abruptly as the test sled entered the water brakes. The head was pulled forward, and a feeling of congestion was perceptible during the 0.6 second of deceleration."

In half a second the scoops of the sled plowed through this basin, which was 190 feet long. Abruptly the deceleration rose to a maximum of 22 g; that is to say, at that moment Stapp's head was 22 times as heavy as its normal weight. One second later the sled reached the second water basin, 260 feet long, in which it finally came to a stop. The wild ride had taken 10 seconds all together.

Flight Surgeon David G. Simons, who was helping to conduct these experiments, noted that "following run, the experimental subject appeared pale and slightly dazed for two or three minutes." Stapp's own report concluded with the sentences: "Within a few seconds after the stop, vision darkened, pulse quickened, and a feeling of faintness was noticed. The tension preceding the run was replaced by elation and a feeling of well-being that lasted for several hours."

The next experiment took place on August 20 of the same year. Stapp, having experimented with dummies, now wanted to test upon his own body the effects of the sudden impact of air at a speed of more than 675 feet per second.

This time he wore a helmet specially designed for the purpose. It covered his head, face, and neck completely, and before the start it was firmly buckled to the headrest. Once again the procedure for strapping the subject to his seat took more than an hour. His harness was reinforced by the addition of a three-inch strap around the chest. This was to ensure that the tremendous deceleration would not break Stapp's neck.

Stapp's forward view was blocked by a rectangular frame holding two doors hinged to the sides. These would open inward by outside wind pressure when a cam mounted at the selected point on the tracks tripped a mechanism releasing the catches. This additional equipment weighed 1,100 pounds, so that eleven rockets had to be mounted on the drive sled, for a total of 49,500 pounds of thrust.

Eleven smoke-wreathed jets of flame spurted from the rear of the sled, setting the grotesque vehicle into motion. After 3½ seconds it was 2,190 feet from its start of the track and had attained its top speed of 736 feet per second. Stapp concentrated his entire attention on the windscreen which was due to open shortly before the rockets burned out, releasing the tremendous blast of the wind against his body.

When the doors opened, Stapp felt the buffet of air against his chest and abdomen and how it made his clothing flutter. For eight tenths of a second the sled coasted freely. Then the braking scoops sent a billow of water into the air and the sled came to a stop after 660 feet, 80 feet before the end of the track. The whole ride had taken a bare ten seconds.

Dr. Simons observed that Stapp's face was flushed, his pulse accelerated, but that he displayed no signs of confusion. In the thorough examination which followed, seven bruises the size of a nickel were discovered on his body; in each was a sand grain which had pierced right through his clothing during the fearsome ride. His left arm had been lashed until it bled by the sleeve of his jacket fluttering in the hurricane blast.

On December 10, 1954, an experiment of great importance was scheduled. Stapp knew that this time he was literally risking his neck. For the heavy windscreen had been entirely removed; Stapp would be under greater stress than ever before.

This time the preparations consumed more than eighty minutes. The crash helmet was adjusted with particular care, the straps drawn tighter than in any of the previous experiments. The chest strap was put on in the last twenty minutes and was pulled tight enough to restrain all rib motion in breathing.

As usual the voice from the loud-speaker began the countdown. At "five" Stapp held his breath; at "zero" the nine powder rockets ignited. They sent the sled hurtling forward like a projectile, unchecked this time by the windscreen which in the past had exerted a strong braking effect. The acceleration mounted to more than 7 g; after 2,770 feet the sled attained the highest speed ever reached by a manned vehicle on the ground: 937 feet per second, i.e., 637 miles per hour.

Later Stapp told a visitor that during those decisive seconds he had felt like "a fly on a bullet." Still under the immediate impression of the murderous test, he recorded: "The acceleration was noticeably greater, the thrust of the seat against the subject's back more violent than in any previous run. The concrete ditch, which was clearly in focus between the tracks before motion began, became a blurred image due to inability to focus and perhaps to vibration of the headrest and helmet. Two seconds after the start vision narrowed to the central fields only and after three seconds there was a visual blackout."

Blind, Stapp nevertheless remained fully conscious for the rest of the infernal ride. Although the whole thing was over in a few seconds, it seemed to him painfully long. The rockets burned out; one tenth of a second later the two sleds parted; three tenths of a second later the braking scoops smashed into the channel of water. Still the sled traveled 690 feet in 1.4 seconds before it came to a stop—a few feet before the end of the track. For one second the deceleration had been greater than 25 g; twice, for brief fractions of seconds, it had actually reached forty times the normal acceleration of gravity.

On entry into the water brakes, the blackness before Stapp's eyes changed to a vivid yellow, and in a flash he caught a glimpse of the water basin before the colossal deceleration crushed him against the groaning straps, smashed mercilessly into him, as though he were being molded in a gigantic press into a new organism, one capable of meeting the demands of technology.

So frightful was the pain that Stapp did not even feel the tornado that raged around him almost at the speed of sound for several seconds. The blood rushed to his head and his eyes burned as though they were being pulled out of their sockets. Vision became a shimmering salmon-colored field—the pupils were impinged against the eyelids and the visual sensation was due to light coming through the lids. "Sensation in the eyes was somewhat like the extraction of a molar without anesthetic," Stapp recalled in his subjective report. It was so bad that he did not feel the straps cutting deep into his skin, leaving bleeding welts.

The torture seemed endless; but when the sled came to a stop again, exactly 6½ seconds had passed since the start. Stapp was utterly exhausted. He could open his eyes only by forcing them open with his fingers, and even then the visual impression of shimmering salmon color persisted. He did not lose consciousness, but he was so confused that he was able to communicate his first impressions only in a fragmentary and disorganized manner.

An oxygen mask was pressed to his face, but he pushed it away and asked to be unstrapped. His shortness of breath gradually diminished after the straps were released. Stapp rose, swaying slightly, but because of his blindness was unable to leave the sled without assistance. His face was purple, and beneath his eyes were swollen, blue-black rings.

After 8 minutes his vision slowly returned. Stapp saw small, vague flecks of light which came and went, until at last they became clearer and remained, coalescing into a gleaming blue surface: the sky above Holloman Air Field, arching over the scene like a great bell.

Stapp had survived a seemingly impossible stress test. He had imposed upon himself an ordeal such as no man in history had been deliberatly put to. His bronchial tubes were still blocked by swollen mucous membranes; he was still bothered by hoarseness and occasional fits of coughing; the welts raised by the straps still burned like fire, but, he concluded his report on the experiment: "There was only a feeling of relief and elation in completing the run and in knowing that vision was unimpaired."

Never before on earth had anyone braked a vehicle as sharply as John Paul Stapp in these merciless experiments on himself. Stapp was not concerned with breath-taking speed in itself, but only with changes in speed, with acceleration and deceleration. His sled was not a racing vehicle in the traditional sense, but rather a simulator, an apparatus intended to simulate the effects of collision, fall, and impact. That was the deeper significance of the cruel game played out at Holloman Field Laboratory and other strangely equipped playgrounds here and there in the world.

Ever-greater speeds, unrelenting accelerations, and dangerous, violent changes of direction represent some of the outstanding stresses imposed upon man by technological advances. In the light of these new strains, which seem to have already reached the limit of tolerance, we must ask whether man is still stronger than his technology, or whether he has made himself the slave of his own ambitious strivings.

When Baron Munchausen amused his friends with the adventurous story of his bold leap upon a flying cannonball, he simplified the problems involved. He knew nothing about acceleration and jolt, nor did his audience raise such troublesome points. The modern rocket-assist-take-off technique, in which a plane is hurled into the air from a ramp by rockets, without a starting run, outdoes Munchausen's fantastic feat, for man and machine are subjected to a load of 28 G. During a fast vertical start of a plane or rocket the forces are smaller, but may persist for minutes. In rocket flight, loads of between 2 G and 9 G are regular. This increase in weight naturally applies to the body fluids, the blood, the internal organs, and the limbs of the passengers.

If a pilot pulls his plane out of a dive, he is under a load of about 4 G for some 3 seconds. If he makes a turn at high speed, he must endure 2 G for 35 seconds; with a smaller radius of curvature this may go up to 5 G for 15 seconds. He cannot adjust the radius of curvature to his taste because at high speed the trajectory of the plane becomes "rigid."

Before World War II a load of from 4 to 6 G was considered the limit of tolerance. In countless stress tests since then human beings have shown that they can endure far higher accelerations. Nine times normal weight is certainly not pleasant, but it does no harm to the body; men can stand such a load for 10 seconds in a seated position and for more than 60 seconds when lying comfortably on their backs, without any signs of blacking out.

Blacking out is a consequence of disturbances of the blood circulation and of breathing. The blood, which is also subject to the increase in weight, is drained to the lower parts of the body. The brain is no longer supplied with adequate blood, and loss of consciousness results.

In a brief and sudden jolt, on the other hand, the blood circulation is not affected. Instead, there are sprains, dislocations, ruptures of tissue, and broken bones when the load exceeds the tolerance limits of the human body. Severe falls can produce 50 to 100 G, the severest kind of accidents far more than 700 G. By way of comparison we may mention that forces up to 20,000 G have been generated in centrifuges, while the greatest weight so far determined for an object on a fixed star is 27 million G.

Since man's technological environment is productive of these and many other stresses, there is a real need for determining the tensile strength of human tissue, the fragility of bones, and the duration of stress tolerable without loss of consciousness, visual disturbances, auditory errors, and lowering of functional efficiency.

The scientist does not plan his tests at random; he bases them upon the loads to be expected in the future. In other words, he is already testing the model of tomorrow's human being, for he combines with his tests of strength the effects of subnormal pressure, excessive pressure, heat, cold, insufficient oxygen, noise, and vibration.

One of the largest human centrifuges in the world was set up in 1952 in the acceleration laboratory at Johnsville, Pennsylvania.

Its spherical light-metal gondola has whirled many an experimental subject into a state of unconsciousness.

The gondola or cabin is suspended from a beam 50 feet long. It is equipped with counterweights to prevent jerky motion. An electric motor brings this super-carrousel to a circular speed of 90 miles per hour within 1½ seconds. After 7 seconds it is whirling around at 175 miles per hour. The stress on the man in the gondola amounts to 40 G.

This enormous centrifuge rotates in a circular concrete chamber. Suspended from the ceiling, accessible from outside, is a glass-walled cockpit for the director of the experiment. The walls of the chamber are also provided with observation windows.

There are several different motors which can be brought into action during the run. The cabin can be partially emptied of air, and the temperature raised. By these measures the test for the volunteer inside the tiny cabin is pushed to the extreme limit of tolerance.

Since the human guinea pig cannot be directly observed while the centrifuge is running, television cameras have been installed inside the gondola. The pictures are transmitted to the laboratory, where, in addition, all the instrument data are registered by automatic recording instruments. Inside the cabin there are even X-ray cameras, so that not only the volunteer's frightfully contorted face can be seen, but also his laboring heart.

A similar modern high-speed centrifuge station was placed in operation in the spring of 1955 at the Institute of Aviation Medicine in Farnsborough, near London. There the 66-foot-long beam, made of steel tubes, rests upon a ring of cast steel which also serves as a heavy flywheel. From the ends of this beam dangle the nacelles for the subjects, each one 33 feet from the center of rotation. The whole centrifuge rotates in a deep, circular concrete pit, in full view of the director of the experiment, whose observation room is above it. Starting time, starting speed, rotational speed, acceleration, and duration of the experiment are pre-determined and regulated by automatic controls throughout. Consequently, every experiment can be faithfully repeated down to the last detail.

In the beam, directly above the center of rotation, sits a special observer who can watch the nacelle directly because he, too, is revolving during the experiment. The subject, the test engineer, and the observer are connected by an intercommunication system. Each one independently can stop the centrifuge. The motors will not start until the volunteer in the gondola has gripped a switch firmly. If he loses consciousness during the test, so that his grip relaxes, an alarm light flashes in the control room. If the engineer in charge misses the signal and does not throw the stopping switch, an automatic mechanism interrupts the experiment 5 seconds later.

The observer has no easy job; he is whirling around himself at one revolution per second when the centrifuge is running at full speed. At this juncture the nacelles are racing around the concrete pit at 115 miles per hour and the passengers are being pressed against their contour beds with a force of 30 G.

Twentieth-century man, like the men of all centuries before him, has many faces—cheerful and grave, joyful and sad, kindly and vindictive. Technology, however, has created a new range of human expression—a set of countenances of man in the grip of physical forces hitherto beyond human experience. These are the faces of man reduced to mere material, flesh becoming putty to the relentless pressure of physical forces.

In wind tunnels tremendous gusts are blasted against the bodies and unprotected faces of human subjects, artificial storms wilder than any of the hurricanes that occur on the surface of the earth. The raving molecules of air dig into the flesh of the cheeks. They force their way through yielding lips into the mouth until the skin rises in crazy waves. They model frightful masks that scarcely resemble anything human.

Acceleration, too, has its characteristic face; it, too, can transform human physiognomy into a gruesome mask. The men who ride the "wheel," as they call the centrifuge, have pictures of themselves no horror film monster can equal. The skin over the cheeks is drawn down sharply, the mouth contorted; the eye sockets are pulled downward and gaping wide. Under the almost-closed eyelids the white of the eye gleams. The whole face is frozen in a horrible grimace.

Flashing such a picture, the owner of it will smilingly inform his distressed friends that this was himself under 10 G or more in the centrifuge. His body, he will say, felt made of lead rather than flesh—though it was unfortunately by no means as tough as metal. Not a pleasant experience; after only 2 seconds, unconsciousness wiped out all pain.

Far from a pleasant experience indeed! In the acceleration laboratory a voice emerging impassively from a loud-speaker requests all persons to leave the centrifuge room. The subject, dressed only in a pair of athletic shorts, lies strapped to the well-padded bed, his face turned toward the ceiling of the tiny cabin. His body is covered with lead wires and contacts for the electro-cardiographs, the electroencephalographs, the manometer, tonicity guage, thermometer.

Now the bare, circular room is empty. A last bell signal. The electric motor rumbles, the "wheel" begins to spin and rapidly reaches high speed.

The man on the torture rack inside the capsule experiences a strange sense of confusion. He feels himself being lifted toward the ceiling of his tiny cabin, but this illusion soon vanishes. Then centrifugal force presses him down upon the bed. He feels himself getting heavier; it is as though the capsule were carrying him upward, and "upward" is always where the ceiling happens to be.

In reality his face is now turned toward the center of the centrifuge, but the subject does not notice this.

His face, as seen on the television screen in the observation room, is already distorted. The load meter continues to climb: 2 G, 4 G, 6 G. From the loud-speaker, eerily and hardly comprehensible, comes the subject's voice: No sensation of speed—arm movement more difficult—increasing pressure in the head—stabbing pain in the eyes.

The load meter is now advancing almost simultaneously with the second hand of the clock. Seven G—the man in the whirling capsule is now as heavy as would be a statue of himself made of solid iron. The test proceeds according to plan. The director orders over the microphone: Read the gauge! The television screen shows the subject trying to read the instrument over his head. Calmly, the observer notes delayed-reaction time. Finally the subject mumbles his reply, and the test engineer records whether the reading was right or wrong.

Eight G—the director orders: "Alarm!" His voice shrieks in the subject's headset. The subject must now move a lever. The stop watch runs on. The subject can no longer lift his hand, but he is able to push it horizontally along the guide rail provided beforehand. Finally the control light flashes; the experiment is a success.

Crackling graph paper rolls out on the instrument table. Automatic styluses draw blue curves, a segment of the subject's life, the history of his heart, his brain, his blood circulation, during those seconds of inhuman stress.

The observers note fogging of vision, loss of hearing, haziness, and finally unconsciousness. With practiced movements medical aides lift the unconscious man from his Procrustean bed—a sample of tormented Homo sapiens whom biologists and physicians will continue to study in detail.

The next subject meets the ordeal standing up in a gondola.

He feels an attack of nausea which he quickly overcomes. Then the increasing force presses down on him. At 2 G he reports in a voice quivering with strain: feeling of heaviness in hands and feet—dizziness—gray mist before the eyes—like milk glass. His legs can no longer support the increased weight; the wheel is brought to a stop sooner than usual.

The third sits up in the gondola. His experience is similar to that of pulling an airplane out of a steep power dive. Tersely, he delivers his reports while the load meter climbs: 2 G—pressure against the buttocks; 3 G—heaviness throughout the body, head held upright with difficulty; 5 G—leg movements impossible, arm movements difficult and uncontrolled, strong tug at chest; 6 G —constricted breathing, veil before eyes, field of vision narrowing, congestion of blood in feet, breathing difficult, holding breath . . . sparks before eyes, loss of vision. The heart and lungs are being pressed downward, but the tormented man no longer feels it; his brain is empty of blood, his senses fade. Unconsciousness releases him. As soon as the load is lessened, consciousness and vision return. Confused, the man clambers out of his seat without assistance at the end of the experiment.

Another submits to the most grueling test of all: hanging head downward. His internal organs, unadjusted to this unnatural direction, are more badly wrenched than in the other experiments. His face becomes strikingly distorted. He feels that his skin is being drawn over his head. The belts supporting him press into his shoulders and thighs, but the tugging pain in his face puts all other sensations in the shade. His head feels as if it were in a vise. At 4 G his brain is already throbbing furiously with pain. His eyes seem to be striving to leap from their sockets. They smart as if sand had been strewn in under the lids. Whatever the volunteer is still able to see appears red as blood.

At 6 G mental confusion ensues. Again, in this agonizing experiment, unconsciousness comes as a relief. Many hours after the experiment is over the man remains dazed, and the stabbing pains in the head linger on, receding only very gradually.

At Wright Field near Dayton, Ohio, human beings are bound to a wheel and rotated horizontally.

This process is an imitation of the observed forces to which pilots of jet planes are subjected when they are compelled to bail out. In his tiny, tightly sealed cabin the flier nowadays literally sits on a powder barrel. Charges of powder blow him, together with his seat, right out of the plane when danger of a crack-up makes it necessary for him to "jump." Immediately afterward he usually begins tumbling rapidly.

The pilot of the rocket research plane X-3 does not climb into his cockpit. Instead, he squeezes into an elevator which the plane sends down to him, and an electric motor raises him up into the belly of the plane. If he is forced to leave the plane while it is hurtling through the air at supersonic speeds, he and his seat are thrown downward and out. After the ejection the seat automatically spreads stabilizing flaps which prevent the dangerous rotation. At a height of about 12,000 feet the pilot parts from his airy throne, the parachute opens, and he sinks slowly to the ground.

For the biologists the problem was: How fast can a man safely rotate around a vertical axis; how much can he take and what goes on inside him on the margin of that limit beyond which wait permanent injury and death? To obtain some answer to these questions, volunteers at Wright Field were strapped to horizontal turntables. These look innocuous compared to the furious giant centrifuges, but for the experimental subjects they are considerably more painful.

The reports on these tests contain not only the usual data, the reactions of heart and brain, the changes in pulse and blood pressure, but some personal observations also: First the feet began to tingle as though they were falling asleep. Then the subject felt the skin of his face being drawn up farther and farther. This was so painful that the concurrent heaviness in the feet was no longer noticed. All feeling concentrated in the head. It was as if the cheeks were being drawn over the eyes—until the hammering pressure in the temples in turn crushed all other sensation and all thoughts.

In these experiments the effects of capital G are felt in two directions at once: toward the feet and toward the head. With smaller forces the feet do not matter so much, but the effects upon the brain do, for there is danger of cerebral hemorrhages. When the human top spins twice a second around his own axis, he suffers no harm. But in real emergencies much higher rotations may be experienced. These merciless experiments and their unequivocal results have led directly to new designs and new methods which slow down or entirely check the whirling motion of ejected fliers.

If the uncanny G forces operate upon the body for less than half a second, the effects which follow from longer accelerations do not occur because there is no time for circulatory disturbances, with all their dramatic consequences, to take place. Survival of a jolt is solely a matter of the tensile strength of tissue and the stamina of the bones.

Where does the actual upper limit lie? How much of a load can man take? In seeking answers to these questions the scientists have been aided by chance. Professor Hugh de Haven, biologist at Cornell University, was fortunate in being able to study the cases of several persons who fell from heights of between 50 and 100 feet and, remarkably, escaped with relatively minor injuries.

It is possible to dive into a swimming pool from a height of 50 feet if the pool is deep enough. I have seen a child who fell headfirst from the second story of a house and suffered only a slight concussion of the brain because the soft garden soil yielded a few inches under the impact. This slight yield was sufficient to save the child's life and health.

Similar factors entered into the cases investigated by De Haven. He measured the imprints in the ground left by the victims. These imprints represented the "deceleration distance," and from that he was able to calculate the jolt the bodies had received. A body falling from a height of 60 feet would be moving at a speed of 60 feet per second at the moment of impact. This corresponded to the speed of an automobile going 40 miles per hour. The impression made in the ground was 4 inches deep. From this De Haven deduced an impact of 150 G lasting one hundredth of a second.

However, the load is not distributed evenly over the whole body. Therefore, the manner in which the falling body strikes the ground is important. The impact to the head, for example, can be much more violent than the impact to the trunk. In the course of his investigations De Haven concluded that the victims had survived top loads of nearly 200 G.

On the basis of such data the scientists have concluded that under favorable circumstances men can withstand loads of between 175 and 200 G. Colonel Stapp, in his deceleration experiments, can therefore risk braking even more sharply, can systematically subject himself to even greater stresses. Undoubtedly Stapp and other experimental subjects the world over will yet have to face more difficult tasks, more painful tests in their push to the very verges to human endurance.

Many people will only shake their heads over these seemingly foolish and incomprehensible tests of human stamina. It has been said again and again: This is flying in the face of Creation; it is challenging Nature, and Nature will strike back; does man think he is omnipotent, or that by such manipulation he can achieve omnipotence for his feeble body?

But those who hold this view forget the matter-of-fact way in which they themselves make use of the technology they deplore. They ignore a significant fact: that they themselves unconsciously brave far greater stresses than their grandfathers or great-grandfathers would ever have done. For our forefathers a trip to Italy was the high point of a lifetime, not merely a casual choice for a summer vacation. How many critics of technology see nothing strange about a flight across the ocean in the company of fifty to a hundred comfortably accommodated passengers? They have merely forgotten the hard road that preceded this particular amenity.

The fearful stress tests we have described are nothing but the preparation for the next stretch of that same road. The preliminaries are merely more exact, more carefully planned, and more ruthless, with human subjects who at their own risk are paving the way for the safety of those who will follow after.

About the Editors

HELEN WRIGHT is an astronomer and writer. She studied at private schools in the United States and Switzerland and was graduated from Bennett Junior College and Vassar College where she was granted a B.A. and M.A. in astronomy.

Miss Wright has worked at the Vassar College Observatory, the Maria Mitchell Observatory, Mount Wilson and Palomar observatories, and the United States Naval Observatory. She is a member of the American Astronomical Society and the History of Science Society.

She is the author of SWEEPER IN THE SKY—A LIFE OF MARIA MITCHELL and of PALOMAR—THE WORLD'S LARGEST TELESCOPE. With Harlow Shapley and Samuel Rapport she edited A TREASURY OF SCIENCE. She and Mr. Rapport are also editors of GREAT ADVENTURES IN SCIENCE, THE CRUST OF THE EARTH, THE GREAT EXPLORERS, and GREAT ADVENTURES IN NURSING.

SAMUEL RAPPORT, an editor by profession, was graduated from Cambridge Latin School and Harvard University. He is a vice president of the publishing firm of Appleton-Century-Crofts. Mr. Rapport and his wife and daughter are residents of Blairstown, New Jersey.